THE
BOOK OF TR
OR
LIBRARY
OF
USEFUL ARTS
1811

Volume II

Edited by Beryl Hurley

Published by Wiltshire Family History Society

Originally printed by
W. Flint, Old Bailey, London
for R. PHILLIPS, No. 7, Great Bridge-street.

The fourth edition, from which these trades are reproduced, was printed in 1811, in three volumes. They are now published in two volumes and the contents of Volume I are listed in the back of this volume.

Pictures, except the Rope Maker, are taken from *Rustic Vignettes for Artists and Craftsmen,* by W.H. Pyne, originally published in London by Rupert Ackermann & Co. in 1824. All pictures are now published by Dover Publications, Inc., 180 Varick Street, New York 10014.

CONTENTS
of
PART II

THE PAVIOUR

The nature of the paviour's business is known to every one who has resided but a short time in any city or large town. The tools required in the work are few, viz. a pick-axe to loosen the earth sufficiently deep to admit the stones; a large wooden hammer; and a birchen broom, with which he brushes the small gravel into the joints between the stones.

The utility of this work, will be obvious, when it is considered that previously to paving the streets of London, Holborn which had long been a principal street, "was so deep and miry, that many perils and hazards were thereby occasioned, as well to the king's carriages passing that way as to those of his subjects." The other streets are described as having been very foul, full of pits and sloughs, perilous and noisome, as well to persons on horseback as on foot. On this account Henry V, about the year 1417, ordered two vessels, each of twenty tons burthen, to be employed at his expence for bringing stone, with which to pave the streets. From this period it appears that London has been gradually paved, according as the several parts became more populous, or were devoted to particular purposes. Smithfield was not paved till the year 1614.

Paris was paved at a much earlier period. Philip II, standing one day at a window of his palace, and observing that the dirt and mire which the carriages in passing threw up, produced a most offensive stench, resolved to remedy the nuisance by causing the streets to be paved; for which purpose he issued his orders in the year 1184: and on that occasion the name of the city, which had been *Lutetia,* on account of its dirtiness (from *lutum* the Latin for clay, mud, or mire,) was changed to Paris.

The stones made use of for paving the coach-ways in the streets of London come chiefly from Aberdeen and Newburgh in Scotland, or from the islands of Guernsey and Jersey. The former are a granite of a reddish colour; the latter are collected on the sea-beach, and are, perhaps, the most durable kind of stone that is used.

Square Guernsey or granite stone paving, laid in the best screened gravel, the stones to be nine inches deep, and the bottom of each stone to contain four-fifths of the superficies of the top, is charged at ten shillings a yard. The curb stone, to the foot-pavement, not less than twelve inches wide and seven inches thick, is charged at about two shillings and three-pence *per foot run.* Yorkshire paving, that is, the stone in the footpaths within the curb, is charged at about eleven-pence per square foot.

The journeyman paviour earns three shillings and tenpence a day, and his labourer two shillings and eight-pence. Gravel is purchased by the load, and the pebbles are bought by the ton-weight.

In no place is the convenience of foot passengers more consulted than in London; there are but few of the streets which have not good footways raised above the carriage-road; whereas, in Paris there is no path distinguished for people on foot; the consequence of which is the loss of many lives every year, by persons being beaten down, and run over by horses and carriages.

In Venice, the pavement is of brick, their churches are sometimes paved with marble, sometimes with mosaic work: in France, it consists of what they call *gres,* a sort of free-stone; in Amsterdam, the middle of the street is stone or flint, and the foot-paths are made with bricks.

THE TURNER

Turning is a very ingenious business. The principal engine made use of in this employment is the *lathe,* which is exceeding-useful for the turning of wood, ivory, and various other materials, such as brass, iron and silver, into a round or oval shape.

This art was well known to the antients, and by them carried to a considerable degree of perfection. It is of great importance in many of the arts of life. The architect uses it for the ornaments both within and without highly finished houses, and the mechanician and natural philosopher have recourse to it not only to embellish their instruments, but to adapt them to their different uses.

There are various kinds of lathes. Some require the aid of one or two men to turn the wheel; but in others the wheel is turned by means of a treadle, by the same man that is employed in turning the wood. The thing to be turned is fixed on the lengthened axis of a smaller wheel, and upon the prop or rest the chisel or other cutting instrument is supported; and being brought to touch the wood while it is swiftly turning round, it takes off shavings to the greatest nicety.

The piece to be turned should be rounded before it be put on the lathe; either with a small hatchet, or with a plane, &c. shaving it down till it is every where nearly of an equal thickness, leaving it a little larger than it is intended to be when finished off.

The young turner should endeavour to acquire the complete management of the gouge and chisel, which are the instruments by far the most frequently used, and the most necessary in this art; by them almost all the soft woods are worked; and as to the hard woods, as box, ebony, ivory, oak, they are scarcely ever turned except by shaving off. In that case gravers are to be used with square, round, or triangular ends. Those should be held horizontally while applied to the wood; but the gouge and chisel must be used obliquely.

When the work is completely turned, it is next to be polished. Soft woods, as the pear-tree, the hazel, and the maple, may be polished with fish skin or Dutch rushes. Fish-skin which is the skin of the shark, is always much better after it has been used, because in its natural state it is too rough for bringing work to a proper degree of polish. The oldest plants of the Dutch rush are the best but before they are used they must be moistened with water. When the work is finished in this way, it is to be rubbed up with a little wax, or olive oil. Ivory, horn, silver, and brass are polished with pumice-stone finely pounded and put upon leather. Different methods, and different substances are made use of, for this purpose by different workmen.

According to Dr. Paley, not a man in a million knows how an oval frame is turned: it may be thus made: Take two ovals of metal exactly of the size of the oval wanted, fix them firmly on the spindle of the lathe, so as to turn round with it: fix between them the wood to be turned, and then it is readily cut with chisels or other tools, as the lathe goes into exactly the figure of the external ovals.

In fixing a lathe, great care should be taken that it be placed in a light situation near a window, and neither so low as to oblige the workman to stoop to see his work, nor so high, that the chips should come in his eyes.

A journeyman in this business may earn a guinea and a half a week, and those who work on toys and smaller articles much more. The lathes used in the nicer sort of turning are very expensive; consequently the stock of a master turner is valuable; and no lad should be brought up to the trade that has not something of a mechanical genius, because there is an almost endless variety in the trinkets made for sale, as may be seen in any large retail shop window.

Ivory is much used by the turner, which is the tooth or tusk of the elephant, growing on each side of his trunk, somewhat in the form of a horn. Ivory is much esteemed for its colour, the fineness of its grain, and its polish. That from Ceylon and Achen is the best, as it never becomes yellow. It is easily stained to any colour.

THE BRUSH-MAKER

The nature of this man's business is making brushes, hair and carpet, brooms, and mops of all sorts; he is generally the manufacturer of wooden coal-hods and of measures for corn and coals.

The wooden part of the brushes is generally of oak, which is cut to its proper size by a large knife fastened down to a block, with a staple at one end, in such a manner, that it is moveable up and down; to the other end is a handle. The wood to be cut is held in the left hand, while the knife is worked with the right. The knife is always kept very sharp; and, by its make and mode of using, hard wood is very readily reduced to any shape and size. This wood, when cut into the proper sizes, is drilled with as many holes as is necessary, and into these the hair is put.

The hair made use of by brush-makers is hogs' bristles, vast quantities of which are imported every year from Germany and Russia, when we are not at war with those powers. These are subject to a heavy duty.

In chusing brushes, observe if the hair is fast bound and if it lies close together; if it is not well bound, and the hair appears to fly out, the brush will never work well; and if the hair is not fast bound, it will come out on the work and disfigure it, as is discoverable from loose hair lying about when the paint is laid on. Brushes in which the hair is fastened with silver wire are superior to those fastened with copper or iron wire, especially when they are to be used with water: brushes for the hat-maker are best fastened with card and wooden pegs instead of wire and the usual cements as they have to be frequently dipped in a boiling, though weak, mixture of water and sulphuric acid.

There are brushes of various sorts, shapes, and sizes; but the structure of them all is the same, or nearly so. When the bristles are sorted, combed, and picked, a certain portion of them is taken and tied together in the middle with string, fine copper, or iron wire, and then doubled: in this double state they are fastened into the wooden stock with hot cement made of melted glue or pitch and rosin. The ends of the hair are now to be cut off, and the surface to be made even or uniform.

Common hearth-brushes and hair brooms are made in a slighter way. As soon as the stock is brought to its proper shape it is drilled, and the *bushes* inserted in the manner above mentioned.

In some brushes the wires are visible on the back; in others the backs are smooth, there being thin slices of wood glued over the wires. The scrubbing brush is sometimes used to dry rub oaken floors; in that case the backs are loaded with lead. In London and its vicinity, where the high wages of female servants render them impertinent and slothful, it has become by custom a part of the man-servant's business to use them, but in the country, where wages are lower, the female servants consider this sort of work theirs beyond dispute, and would ridicule a man, "for working women's work." In this business Mr. Thomasin of Birmingham has obtained a patent for a new method of making hearth brushes, perhaps more ingenious than useful; these are so constructed as to conceal the hair in a metal case, by means of rack work.

Mops are made of woollen yarn spun for the purpose. Besides these there are other kinds of mops manufactured of woollen rags, which are collected by poor women from the dust taken from dunghills, &c.

The coal-hods are usually made of oak, with two wooden or iron handles on the sides; they are not so neat as copper ones, or as those made of iron and varnished: but they are much cheaper, and will last much longer than iron hods.

Great nicety is required in making corn measures; they must contain a certain exact quantity. The standard for measuring corn, salt, coals, and other dry goods, is the Winchester gallon, and it must contain 272¼ cubic inches; the bushel contains eight such gallons, or 2178 inches.

A journeyman in this business will earn a guinea or thirty shillings a week; the profits to masters are pretty considerable where the returns are great.

Such are the divisions of labour in this country, that the same persons do not make the brushes and the long handles, these last are made by turners who are thus employed by the master brush-maker. In Kent-street, and several other places, there are broomstick manufactories. The making of birch brooms is a distinct and profitable trade. The birch will grow in land which is fit for hardly any thing else. Ground covered with moss has been known to produce birch-trees so well, that in a few years they have sold for ten pounds per acre, and the after produce has been considerably increased.

Besides broom-makers, who are constant customers for the birch; hoop-benders are considerable purchasers of the same article. The largest trees are often bought by turners, and the wood is used for yokes and other instruments of husbandry. In the northern countries of Europe, birch wood is used for wheels of carriages.

THE TAYLOR

The Taylor makes clothes for men and boys, and riding-habits for ladies. In a taylor's shop where much business is carried on, there are always two division of workmen: first the foreman, who takes the measure of the person for whom clothes are to be made, cuts out the cloth, and carries home the newly finished garments to the customers. The others are mere working taylors, who sit cross-legged on a bench; of these very few know how to cut out, with any degree of skill, the clothes which they sew together.

The tools requisite in the business of a taylor are very few and unexpensive: the shears for the foreman, who stands to his work; for the others, a pair of scissars, a thimble, and needles of different sizes. In the thimble there is this peculiarity, that it is open at both ends. Besides these there are required some long slips of parchment for measure, and an iron called a *goose;* with this, when made hot, they press down the seams, which would otherwise take off from the beauty of the goods. The stand for the iron is generally a horse-shoe rendered bright by wear of the iron. The foreman, or master, (for where the trade is not extensive the master cuts out, measures gentlemen, and carries home the clothes,) has a box which contains buckram, tapes, bindings, trimmings, buttons,. &c. with which every master taylor should be furnished, and from which they derive very large profits.

The taylor in London purchases his broad-cloths of the woollen-draper who buys his goods from the Blackwell-Hall factory, or from the clothiers settled in the west of England. At Bristol fair, which is held in September, for fourteen days, an immense number of broad-cloths are sold by clothiers, who assemble there, and hire shops for the purpose. The taylors deal also with the mercer for fancy waistcoats and other articles of dress; with the haberdasher for all his small wares; but when he makes clothes for officers, he must go to the gold and silver lace-makers for the necessary ornaments.

The wages of a journeyman taylor are regulated by act of parliament, and he now has four shillings and six-pence a day: the trade is over-stocked with hands, though men that are sober, industrious, and skilful in their business, are seldom out of employment. In times of general mourning for any branch of the Royal Family the wages of the men are double, but they work more hours in the day.

A writer on this subject says, that a master "ought to have a quick eye, to steal the cut of a sleeve, the pattern of a flap, or the shape of a good trimming at a glance: any bungler may cut out a shape when he has the pattern before him; but a good workman takes it by his eye in the passing of a chariot, or in the space between the door and a coach: he must be able not only to cut for the handsome and well-shaped, but bestow a good shape where nature has not granted it: he must make the clothes sit easy in spite of a stiff gait or awkward air; his hand and head must go together; he must be a nice cutter, and finish his work with elegance.

The woollens in which the taylor principally deals, is a vast branch of English manufacture. And so jealous are we of this trade, that besides the precautions taken to use our own wools ourselves, we insist upon selling them ourselves, and of carrying them to the places where there is a demand for them.

THE SHOE-MAKER

There are few trades more useful than that of the Shoe-maker, and perhaps not many that are more profitable when it is carried on to a considerable extent. Some shoe-makers carry on a snug private trade without any show; others have large shops, and exhibit in them shoes of all sorts, for ladies and gentlemen, together with boots, gaiters, and spatterdashes.

The master shoe-maker, or, if he is in a very large way, his foreman, measures his customers, and cuts out the leather for his work-people to put together. In some instances especially in the country, he is the leather-cutter to all the little traders in the surrounding villages. In this case he buys the leather in skins and half hides from the dresser, and cuts them out into soles and upper leathers, which he either uses in his own business, or sells, to those who cannot afford to go to the wholesale market.

To render this business profitable, a considerable degree of knowledge is required with regard to the properties of leather, and an accurate judgement to cut the leather in such a manner as to yield the greatest quantity with the least waste.

The master cuts out an upper leather of a shoe to a paper pattern which lies upon it. A small leaden weight is placed on the skin at the corner to keep it from slipping: on his left lies the hammer which he uses to beat down any rough parts which stand on the inside of the leather, and on his right hand is a pair of pincers, which are made with teeth, in order to gripe (sic) the leather tight in the act of stretching it.

The journeyman joins the upper leather to the sole of a shoe. On his bench near him are his awl, his knife, and a stone with which he sharpens his tools. Before him, on his right, are the hammer and lapstone, and on the other side a tub of water, in which he keeps a quantity of wax in balls. These are the principal implements necessary for his trade. He sews the leather together with thread waxed over, and thereby made a strong and durable substance: as, however, he makes no use of a needle, to the end of the thread is fastened a hog's bristle, which guides the thread through the holes made in the leather with an awl.

Journeymen in this trade are distinguished into women's shoe-makers, and those who make shoes and boots for men. Few can follow both branches with advantage; the greater ingenuity is required in manufacturing women's shoes, because the seams must be neater, as the materials are much finer.

Women are employed to bind shoes of all kinds, and to sew the quarters together of those that are made of silk, satin, and stuffs.

Shoes and boots are made on *lasts* which are manufactured of some soft wood by means of an engine or knife. The same man that makes *lasts*, makes also the wooden heels for women's shoes. The *last* for shoes is made of a single piece of wood to imitate the foot; but that for boots is slit into two parts, between which a wedge is driven when the boot-leg is wished to be stretched.

It appears from history that the Jews, long before the Christian era, wore shoes made of leather or wood; those of their soldiers were sometimes formed out of brass or iron. The Grecian shoes generally reached to the middle of the leg. The Romans used two kinds of shoes: the *calceus*, which covered the whole foot, something in the shape of our shoes; and the *solea*, or slipper, which covered only the sole of the foot, and was fastened with leathern thongs. The *calceus* was worn with the toga when a person went abroad, and slippers were put on during a journey and at feasts. Black shoes were worn by the citizens of ordinary rank, and white ones by women. Red shoes were put on by the chief magistrates of Rome on the days of ceremony.

In Europe, about a thousand years ago, the greatest princes wore shoes having the upper part of leather and the under of wood. In the reign of William Rufus the shoes of the great had long sharp points, stuffed with tow, and twisted like a ram's horn. The clergy preached against these points: they continued, however, to increase till the reign of Richard II, when they were tied to the knees with chains of silver or gold. At length parliament interfered by an act in the year 1463, and prohibited the use of shoes or boots with pikes exceeding two inches in length: and shoe-makers were forbidden, under severe penalties, to make them contrary to the statute.

A journeyman shoe-maker, if he be a good hand, sober, and industrious, will earn thirty shillings a week.

Shoe-makers use large quantities of Morocco leather, which is the skin of a goat, dressed in sumac, or gall; and coloured at pleasure: it is used also for trunks, book-binding, and various other work that requires neatness.

THE TRUNK-MAKER

The persons employed in this trade make trunks, chests, portmanteaus, cases for holding plate and knives, and buckets.

Trunks, of which there are various shapes and sizes, are generally made with wood and covered with leather, or the skins of horses or seals dressed with the hair on, and they are lined with paper. To some trunks there are a number of thin iron cramps put on for the sake of strength. Those which are well finished are ornamented with several rows of brass-headed nails. Those intended for holding a service of plates, which is usually sent to the banker's for safety, when the family to whom it belongs retire to their country residence, are divided by several partitions, and lined with baize or cloth.

Travelling-trunks are fastened either before or behind the carriage with leathern straps, and buckles, or by means of chains. A patent was taken out some years since for a method of fastening trunks and portmanteaus to travelling carriages, so as to defy the art of robbers, who in and near the metropolis are on the watch to cut off trunks from coaches as they come in or go out of town.

Buckets are formed of strong and stout leather soaked and boiled. They are very useful in extinguishing houses which have taken fire. Most large houses in the country have fifty or sixty of these, as well as a fire-engine, in case of accident; but it generally happens, through the inattention of servants, that if a fire breaks out neither engine nor buckets are fit for use.

Water is sometimes raised out of deep wells by what is called a chain of buckets, that is a number of buckets, attached to a chain or rope, which by the turning of the wheel descend into the water and are brought up full.

Trunk-makers often use in very neat-work, shagreen, which is a kind of grained leather prepared from the skin of a fish, by exposing it to the weather, being first covered with bruised mustard seed, and afterwards tanned. The best shagreen comes from Constantinople, and is extremely hard; but being soaked in water it becomes soft and pliable, and adapted to the use of case-makers. It takes any colour, as red, green, black, &c. and is frequently counterfeited by morocco formed like shagreen; but morocco scales, which is not the case with shagreen.

Journeymen in this business will earn a guinea or thirty shillings a week.

THE WHEELWRIGHT

The business of the wheelwright consists in making the wood work for wheels, putting the parts together and fixing on the iron.

A wheel is composed of several parts; as the *nave,* which is the centre piece, the *spokes,* which are inserted at one end of the nave, and at the other into the *fellies,* which make up the outside rim. These three parts constitute a wheel; but for the sake of giving strength to the whole, some iron work is used: this we shall describe in its proper place.

The nave is that short thick piece of wood in the centre of each wheel, which receives the axle-tree, with holes ready to receive the spokes, which are made to fit in accurately. When the spokes are fitted in the nave the rim or fellies, are next put on the spokes. Each felly is of sufficient length to receive two spokes, so that if there be twelve spokes in a wheel, the rim consists of six pieces or fellies.

The nave is bound at each end on the outside with strong iron hoops, called knave bands: within-side also there is a ring of iron called the *wisher,* to prevent the hole from wearing by the friction of the axle. To the outside rim or fellies is an iron tire fastened with very strong nails or spikes. The parts of the tire are made red hot before they are put on the wheels, in order that they may burn a small depth in the wheel, or at least all that roughness which might hinder it from lying flat with the wood: besides, by being in this state, they may be easily bent, so as to conform most accurately with the curve of the wheel. Another advantage is, that iron when hot expands, and as it becomes cold, it contracts into shorter length: and as the tire of the wheel contracts, it must have a tendency to draw the several parts of the fellies close together. To give the man power over his work, the wheel is placed in a sort of pit made in the floor, on the sides of which the nave may rest, so that little more than half of the wheel stands above the surface. Large pincers enable him to bring the red hot iron from the fire, and place it on the wheel. He uses an axe with a bended blade for hollowing out the fellies.

By thus scooping out the wood, the grain is often so much cut and injured as to weaker it in a great degree. To remedy this, a method has been invented of bending timber into a circular form, so that the whole rim of the wheel consists of not more than two pieces, which are cased with a tire in a single piece. By this mode of construction, the circumference of the wheel is every where equally strong, and much more durable than wheels made in the usual form, though not more than half the quantity of wood is employed.

Elm which is used by wheelwrights for axle-trees is also much in use for chopping blocks, not being liable to chip. Carvers make use of it for foliage, and other curious works of fancy.

Wheelwrights in the country are the makers also of carts and waggons: the wood they principally use is elm, and some oak. Their business is a very laborious one, and requires that no lad should be brought up to it who does not possess a strong constitution: a journeyman will earn from a guinea to thirty shillings a week.

THE IRON-FOUNDER

Although iron is not esteemed the most precious metal, it is beyond all question the most useful. It is employed in three different states, each having peculiar properties, by which it is applicable to various purposes.

The first is *cast iron,* the second *wrought* or malleable iron, and the third is called *steel.*

Our business at present is with the cast-iron manufactory. It will be readily conceived that this business requires great strength, and a constitution that will bear a vast degree of heat.

Iron is dug out of the earth in the form of stones, and in this state it is called ore. The richest ores, that is, those which yield most pure metal, are heavy, and of a brownish colour, inclining to a red.

Before the metal can be extracted the ore must be roasted or calcined: that is done by a different process in different places: at the iron-works in Staffordshire, after the ore is dug, they calcine it in the open air with small charcoal, wood, or sea-coal, in order to break it in small pieces. This process requires three days. But at Forest-Dean, in Gloucestershire, the ore is calcined in kilns made like common lime-kilns: these are filled up to the top with coal and ore, one layer upon another alternately: and then setting fire to the bottom layer of coal, it burns till the coal is wasted away. By this means the ore becomes brittle, but the metal is not fused.

It is now taken to the furnace to be melted, or as it is usually termed, to be *smelted,* that is, to extract the metal from the dross. The furnace is built of brick, and is about twenty-four feet square on the outside, and near thirty feet in height within the middle or widest part of which is not above eight or ten feet, the top and bottom being brought into a narrower compass, something like the shape of an egg. Behind the furnace are fixed two pair of bellows, which are worked by means of a water wheel: and they are contrived so as to play alternately, the one giving its blasts while the other is rising: but in many founderies, the bellows used are constructed after Mr. Wilkinson's plan, by which a regular and uniform blast is continually produced. Holes are left in the furnace, which may be opened at any time to take away the scoria or dross, or to permit the metal to flow out.

The furnace is filled with ore, and charcoal or coke, and sometimes lime-stone is added as a flux. The ore gradually subsides into the hottest part of the furnace, where it is melted and the metallic parts, being the heaviest, fall to the bottom, where there is a passage made for the purpose of taking off the scum. As soon as there is a sufficient quantity of metal in a complete and strong state of fusion, it is let out by a tap-hole into furrows made in an immense bed of sand that lies before the mouth of the furnace: the large mass, which sets in the main furrow, is called by the founders a *sow,* and the lesser or side furrows are termed *pigs* of iron. The metal is generally made so hot before it is drawn off, that it will not only run to a great distance, but will keep boiling for some time in the sand.

For chimney-backs, hearths of ovens, the fronts of stoves, and other small articles, the founder takes the metal out of the receiver in large ladles, from which he pours it into moulds of fine sand.

But for the more intricate cases of iron foundry as casting of cylinders for steam engines or pipes with various branches, moulds are formed of loam or clay, which are made nearly in the same manner as the moulding of plaister for busts, &c.

When the furnaces are once at work, they keep them constantly employed for many months together, never suffering the fire to slacken night or day, but still supplying the wasting of the fuel and the ore with fresh materials poured in at the top.

The excessive and long continued ignition kept in these furnaces gradually wastes the brick work, till the sides, which are many feet thick, become unable to sustain the weight of the melted metal; so that it has sometimes been known to burst out suddenly in a violent and dreadfully destructive stream. At certain intervals, therefore, the fire ought to be allowed to go out, whatever may be the expence of rekindling it, in order to examine and repair the furnace.

Three tons or 6000 pounds of iron are sometimes run off in 24 hours, with the application of the bellows, while the heat without these would scarcely melt a single hundred weight in the same time.

THE COPPER-PLATE PRINTER

The principal things requisite in this business are ink, and a press called a rolling-press, to distinguish it from the common printing press. The art of copper-plate printing owed its origin to accident. In the year 1460, a goldsmith, at Florence, happened to pour some melted sulphur on an engraved plate, and found the exact impression of the engraving left the cold brimstone marked with the black taken out of the strokes by the liquid sulphur; he attempted to do the same on silver plates, with wet paper, by rolling it; and this succeeded: hence the principle of the rolling-press. The art was not applied in England, till the reign of king James I.

The rolling-press may be distinguished into two parts, the *body* and the *carriage*; the body consists of two cheeks, or upright posts, joined at top and bottom by cross pieces and placed perpendicularly on a wooden stand or foot, which sustains the whole press. From this foot rise four other perpendicular pieces, joined also by cross ones: this may be considered as the carriage, because it serves to sustain a smooth even plank, upon which the engraved plate is placed.

Into the cheeks are inserted two wooden cylinders, the ends of which being much smaller than the bodies, and called *trunnions*, and turn in the cheeks between two pieces of wood, in form of half-moons, lined with polished iron to prevent friction.

The spaces left vacant by the trunnion are filled with pasteboard or paper, that they may be raised or lowered at discretion, so as only to leave the space between them necessary for the carriage of the plank, loaded with the plate, paper, and cloths, which consist of swan's-skin and a piece of broad-cloth.

To one of the trunnions of the upper roller is fastened a cross, consisting of two levers, the arms of which give a motion to the upper rollers, and that again to the under one, so that the plank is drawn by this means backwards and forwards.

The best ink that is used in this business comes from Frankfort on the Maine, and it goes by the name of Frankfort black. It comes over in cakes; and is ground by the printer with a muller on an ink-stone; a palette-knife is also used in this part of the business.

The press and the ink being prepared, the printer takes a small quantity of this ink on a rubber made of linen rags, with which he smears the whole face of the plate, as it lies on a grate over a small fire made of old coal.

The plate being sufficiently inked, the printer takes it to a part of the bench called a jigger, and wipes it first with a rag, then with the hand, over which he has rubbed a piece of whiting. The great art consists in wiping the plate perfectly clean, without taking the ink out of the engraving. The plate thus prepared is laid on the plank of the press; over the plate is spread the paper, which has been previously moistened; and the arms of the cross are now to be pulled, and by that means the plate with its furniture is carried between the rollers, over which are the swan's-skin and broad-cloth: these pinching very strongly, yet equally in every part, force the moistened paper into the strokes of the engraving, whence brings away the ink.

Some works require to be passed through the press twice, and once sufficient for others, according as the engraving is more or less deep, or as the print is required to be of a lighter or darker shade.

After the prints are taken off, the plate is rubbed over with olive oil to prevent its rusting, and set by again for a new impression. If the strokes get filled within and hardened, in the course of working, the plates are boiled in strong ley before the oil is applied.

It is said that Earl Stanhope has introduced such improvements in the art of engraving, as will enable the artist to take off from a well engraved plate, at least ten thousand impressions.

Thus the paintings of the greatest masters are multiplied to a boundless number; and the lovers of the polite arts in every part of the globe, are enabled to enjoy those advantages from which their situations seemed to have deprived them.

A journeyman copper-plate printer will earn forty shillings a week. And from a strongly engraved plate three or four thousand good impressions may be taken; and even then the plate may be repaired, and fitted up for other editions.

THE PAINTER

The artist paints portraits, historical pieces, landscapes, sea-pieces with shipping, &c. Some painters have peculiar talents for one department of the art, and some for the others but it rarely happens that the same man excels in them all, or even in more than one or two.

A portrait-painter, in large, is however frequently well skilled in history but an artist who paints in miniature is often unacquainted with any other part of the profession. Some painters who can execute almost any thing else, in a masterly manner, have no idea of shipping, which requires a considerable degree of nautical knowledge.

The implements made use of in this art are, a stone and muller to grind the colours; an operation which is sometimes performed with oil, and sometimes with water: hence the distinction between *painting in oil,* and *painting in water colours.* A palette and palette-knife are also required; the *latter* to take off the paint from the stone; and the *former,* which is made of walnut-tree or mahogany, is that on which the artist puts his colour for immediate use. The pencils or brushes are made of camel's hair, badger's hair, or hogs bristles.

The stick the painter uses is about a yard long, with cotton wool tied round the end in a piece of soft leather, to prevent it scratching the picture. On this the artist rests his right hand, to keep steady. The canvas for the intended picture is placed on a wooden frame, called an *easel,* which is so constructed, by means of holes and pegs, that it may be raised higher or lower at pleasure.

The earning of an artist cannot be defined: he is paid according to his talents, and to the celebrity which he is acquired. Some persons will require a hundred guineas for a piece which another of inferior merit, or little known to the public, would be glad to perform for a twentieth part of that sum.

THE ENGRAVER

Engraving on copper is employed in representing different subjects, as portraits, historical pieces, landscapes, &c. either after paintings, or after designs made for that purpose. It is performed either with the *graver,* the *dry point,* or with *aquafortis.*

The tools necessary for engraving in the first method are gravers, a scraper, burnisher, an oil-stone, a sand-bag, an oil-rubber, and some good charcoal.

The gravers are instruments of tempered steel, fitted in to a wooden handle. They are either square, or in the lozenge form; the first is used in cutting very broad strokes, and the other for fainter and more delicate lines.

The scraper is a three-edged tool for scraping off the burr or roughness raised by the graver.

Burnishes are for rubbing down lines that may be cut too deep, or for taking out any scratches or defects in the copper; they are made of hard steel, well rounded and polished.

The oil-stone is for sharpening the gravers, and the oil-rubber and charcoal for polishing the plate when necessary.

The sand-bag or cushion is for laying the plate upon, for the conveniency of turning it round in any direction: this is principally used by engravers of writing.

Having the copper, tools, and drawing ready, the first thing is to lay the design on the plate: for this purpose, the plate is to be covered over with a thin skin of virgin wax; and the drawing or picture is to be copied on paper with a black-lead pencil, or any matter that is free from gum: this paper is to be laid upon the plate with its penciled side upon the wax, and pressed all over so completely, that when the paper is withdrawn the impression may remain upon the waxed plate; then with a sharp-pointed tool trace the design through the wax on the copper. The plate is now to be warmed, and the wax cleaned off; after which the engraving is to be finished by means of the gravers.

The dry-point or needle, so called because not used till the grounds taken off the plate, is principally employed in the extremely light parts, water, sky, drapery, &c.

Etching is a method of engraving on copper, in which the lines or strokes, instead of being cut with a tool or graver, are put in with aquafortis or nitrous acid, which is thus performed: the copper-plate is first warmed, and then thinly covered with varnish; it is then to be blackened over with the smoke of a wax candle.

The *ground* being now *laid,* and suffered to cool, the next operation is to transfer the design to the plate. For this purpose, the drawing must be traced on oiled paper, with pen and ink, having some ox's gall mixed with it. Another piece of white paper must be rubbed with flake-white, and laid on the varnished copper, with the white side next the plate: upon this is to be put the traced oil paper, and fastened with a piece of bordering wax to the copper.

When this is done, all the lines in the tracing must be gone over with a blunt etching needle, by which means the lines will be transferred to the ground when the papers are taken away.

The plate is now prepared for drawing through the lines which have been marked upon the ground. For this, etching points or needles are employed, leaning hard or light, according to the degree of strength required in the lines.

A margin or border of wax is now to be formed all round the plate, to hold the aquafortis when it is poured on; where it is to be left till the operation is completed. The *biting in* of the plate, as it is called, is the most uncertain part of the process and nothing but experience can enable a person to know when the plate is sufficiently bit.

When the acid has been on long enough to bite the lines that are to be the faintest, the aquafortis is poured off, the plate washed and dried, and those lines that are to be made no deeper must be stopped with turpentine varnish, mixed with a little lamp black, and laid on with a camel's hair pencil; and when thoroughly dry, the aquafortis may be poured on again, to bite the other lines that are required to be deeper.

When the biting-in is finished, the bordering wax, and ground are to be taken off, the plate cleaned, and an impression taken upon paper by a copper-plate; which impression is called a *proof*.

In almost all engravings on copper that are executed in the stroke manner, etchings, and graving are combined; the plate being generally begun by etching, and finished with the graver. Landscapes, architecture, and machinery, are subjects that receive most assistance from the art of etching; it is not so applicable to portraits and historical designs.

The screen that is suspended before the window is to keep off the glare of light, which would be mischievous to the engraver's business. The screen consists of four laths joined at their ends, and covered on both sides with silver-paper.

The art of engraving is ascribed to a goldsmith at Florence, who, having placed a sheet of oiled paper under a plate of silver that was engraved, and on which by accident he had laid a heavy weight, was surprised to find a complete impression of the plate on the paper.

THE STATUARY

This artist carves images and other ornaments in stone, marble, &c. The art is one of those in which the antients surpassed the moderns. Phidias was the greatest statuary among the former, and Michael Angelo among the latter.

Statues are formed with the chisel, of several substances, as stone, marble, and plaster; they are sometimes cast of various kinds of metal, particularly gold, silver, brass, and lead.

When a statue is to be formed of stone, marble, &c. a drawing is first made of the subject intended to be carved; a model is next made, by laying a mass of moist clay on a board, and reducing it to shape and form with knives and spattles. Sometimes a model is made without any previous drawing, and sometimes the stone is cut from a drawing without a model.

The marble or stone is carved with steel chisels of different sizes, and a wooden maul or mallet. The statue is not made in a single piece, but of several, which when finished are fastened together, with a cement of the powder of calcined alabaster, called plaster of Paris; this is mixed with water to the thickness of batter, which in a short time becomes as hard as the marble itself, and is as durable. The earnings of a statuary are as varied as those of a painter.

The Parian marble is most celebrated; and from this, which is of a most beautiful white; the greatest part of the Grecian statues were made. It is also called *statuary* marble, and is generally supposed to have had its name from the island Paros, one of the Cyclades in the AEgean sea, where it was found:

by others the name is derived from Agoracritus Parius, a famous statuary, who gave it celebrity by cutting a statue of Venus from it.

Among the many statues of antiquity cut out of this marble, was that of Laocoon and his two sons, which is mentioned by Pliny, and has escaped the injuries of time.

Almost all white marbles now go under the name of Parian marble; and among the workmen they have the common name of alabaster, though they come from different places, as Spain, some parts of France, Italy, &c. Marble is also found in this country, but not in very large quantities.

Daedalus has been celebrated as the inventor of statues, but it is certain that there were statuaries before his time. He was, however, the first person that found the method of making them appear as if they were alive. Till his time statues were made with their feet joined together: he formed his otherwise; he gave them the attitudes of people walking and acting.

Statues are usually distinguished into four general kinds. The *first* are those less than life, of which kind are the statues of great men, of kings, and of the gods themselves. The *second* are those equal to the life; with these the ancients celebrated the deeds of men eminent for learning or valour. The *third* are those that exceed life; among which some surpassed the life once and a half; these were for monarchs and emperors, and those double the life for heroes. The *fourth* kind were still larger; these were called colossuses, or colossal statues. Of this last, the most eminent was the colossus of Rhodes, one of the wonders of the world, a brazen statue of Apollo, so high that ships passed in full sail between its legs. It was the workmanship of Chares, who spent twelve years in making it.

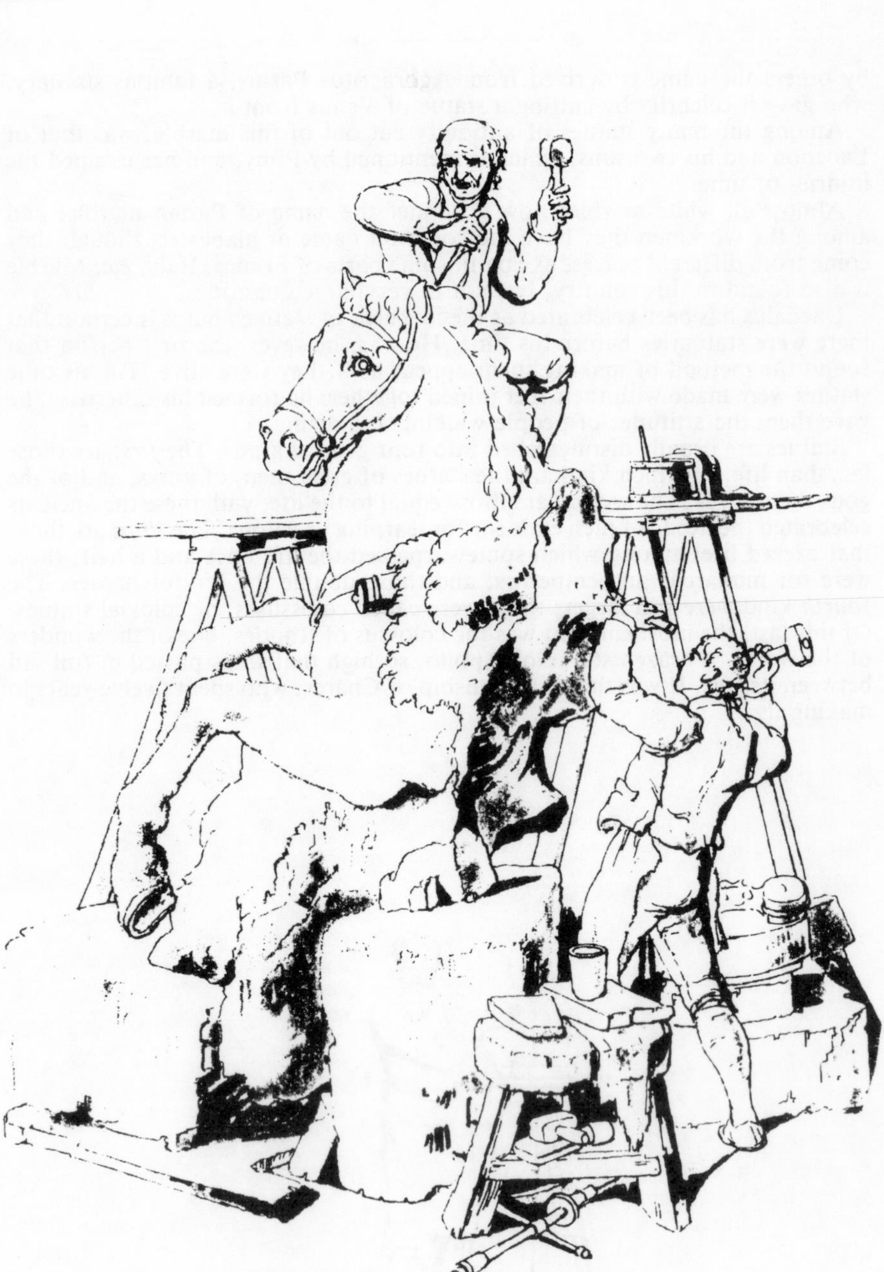

THE BREWER

The art of brewing is of very high antiquity, but in no country has it been carried to greater perfection than in our own. The different counties are, many of them, celebrated for their peculiar ales, and London porter is famous in almost all parts of the civilized world. Different as these several sorts of liquor are, they are nevertheless composed of the same materials variously prepared.

Malt liquor, in general, is composed of water, malt, hops, and a little yeast: and the great art is to find out the proper proportions of each ingredient, to what degree of heat the water must be raised before it is poured on the malt and how best to work it afterwards.

There are two kinds of malt, distinguished by the colour; these are called *brown* and *pale* malt, and they depend on the degree of heat that is used in drying. The malt which is dried by a very gentle heat differs in its colour but little from the barley; but if exposed to a higher temperature, it acquires a deeper hue, till at length it becomes of a dark brown.

When the malt is made, it must be coarsely ground in a mill, or, what seems to be still better, bruised between rollers; it is then fit for the brewer, in whose hands the process of making beer is completed.

The first part of the operation is called *mashing*, which is performed in a large circular vessel. This vessel has a false bottom, pierced with small holes, fixed about six or eight inches above the real bottom. There are two side-openings in the interval between the bottoms. By the one water is conveyed into the vessel, and by the other it is drawn off. When the malt is put on the false bottom of the *mash-tun*, the water, being at a proper heat, is admitted, by means of the side pipe, from the copper, which is contained within the brickwork. The water first fills the space between the false and real bottom; then forcing its way through the small holes in the false bottom, it soaks into the malt, and when all the water is let in, the process of *mashing* begins. The object of this part of the operation is to effect a perfect mixture of the malt with the water, so that the sweet part of the grain may be extracted by the fluid: for this purpose the mass is kept constantly stirred by means of iron rakes, or long wooden poles.

In large breweries, such as that in Chiswell-street, the process of mashing cannot be performed by human labour, it is therefore effected by machinery that is kept moving by means of the steam-engine. As soon as the mashing is completed, the tun is covered in to prevent the escape of heat, and in this state it is suffered to remain till all the sweetness of the malt is extracted; then the side spigot is withdrawn, and the clear wort allowed to run off into a lower or boiling-copper. The heat of the water used in mashing should be about 180° of Fahrenheit's thermometer. Before the goodness of the malt is exhausted it is usual to pour upon it two or three waters, but the wort which is drawn off the first is by much the richest. The proportion of malt to the water depends on the strength of the liquor. It is said that good small beer may be brewed at the rate of thirty gallons to a bushel of malt, and excellent ale may be made in the proportion of one bushel of malt to five or six gallons of water.

The wort when run into the lower copper is to be boiled with a certain quantity of hops; the stronger the wort, the more hops are required; the common proportion in private families is a pound of hops to a bushel of malt. When the hops are mixed with the wort in the copper, the liquor is made to boil; and it must be kept boiling as fast as possible, till, upon taking out a little of the liquor, it is found to be full of small flakes, something like curdled soap.

The boiling copper is, in small concerns, uncovered, but in large breweries it is fitted with a steam-tight cover, from the centre of which passes a cylindrical pipe, that terminates in several branches in the upper, or mashing-copper; thus the steam produced by boiling, instead of being wasted, is let into the cold water of the upper copper, by which it is made almost hot enough for mashing without any additional expence of fuel; the steam carries also with it the flavour of the hops, which, when the operation is carried on differently, is lost in the air.

When the liquor is sufficiently boiled, it is drawn out into a number of shallow tubs, called coolers, in which it remains till it is cool enough to be submitted to fermentation. Liquor made from pale malt, and intended for immediate use, need not be cooler than 75° or 80°, and can of course be made in almost every part of the summer; but that which is for keeping should not be hotter that 65° or 70 when it is put together for fermentation.

From the coolers the liquor is transferred into the fermenting or working-tun, in which it is well mixed with yeast, in the proportion of one gallon of yeast to four barrels of beer. This part of the process takes from 18 to 48 hours, according to the state of the weather.

The last part of the operation is that of transferring the liquor from the working-tun to the barrels, when the fermentation is completed. For a few days there will be a copious discharge of yeast from the bung-hole, during which the barrels must from time to time be carefully filled up with fresh liquor. After this discharge is finished the barrels are bunged up, and the beer is fit for use in the course of a few weeks.

Common report says that in addition to malt and hops, a variety of other ingredients are used, and none of them of the most wholesome nature.

So much for the brewing of malt liquor on a large scale. We shall now give our readers a method very generally pursued by families for brewing their own ale, which practice is getting general from a conviction of the very great unwholesomeness of ale, &c. from some of the public breweries.

Boil twelve gallons of water, put it into a tub with about two gallons of cold water, let it stand until the steam is sufficiently off to reflect your face with ease to yourself; put in the malt, stir it well up, and let it stand three hours. This will produce about seven gallons: after this, mash again with about twelve gallons of water more, and let it stand about two hours, stirring it well, and frequently, boil the first gently in the mean time, after being run off from the grains for nearly three quarters of an hour with three quarters of a pound of hops, strain it, boil the other in the same manner; mix it with the first let it now stand till it is about blood warm or as warm as new milk then put in a quarter of a pint of yeast, work the whole if possible in one vessel let it stand till next afternoon, then tun it in perfectly clean barrels: it ought to work after tunning, a week or ten days; in a few weeks it will be fit for use.

Malt is used also for distilling spirituous liquors. For this purpose it is ground, and the wort taken as in common breweries: this is fermented, and then it is called *wash*, which is put into a still about three parts full. A brisk fire is made under it till the wash is nearly boiling, when the head of the still is fixed on and luted to the worm in the worm-tub. The fire is allowed to decrease till the spirit begins to run. The first produce is called low wine, which is distilled a second time, and then it is pure malt spirit.

Compound distillers mix with malt spirits, juniper-berries, aniseeds, &c. and distil the whole over again, the produce of which is gin, spirit of aniseed, &c.

which, though useful in certain medical cases, never fail to injure and debilitate the constitution when drunk as a common beverage.

Distillers obtain a great quantity of spirit from sugar, treacle, and molasses, in the same way as they do from malt; to these they are always obliged to have recourse in those years in which there has been a scanty crop of corn. The revenue of the state is greatly enriched by distilleries, but the morals and health of the people are unquestionably injured by them.

Rum is distilled from sugar, and the sugar cane, in the West Indies; that sold in Europe is generally very much *cooper'd*, that is, adulterated, before it comes into the consumer's possession. Brandy is extracted from wine by distillation. French brandy is esteemed the best, on account of the superior quality of the wines made in France. The brandy made in Cogniac, Bourdeaux, and Rochelle, bears the highest price. Brandy distilled a second time is called *spirit of wine*; and this, after another rectification, is called pure *alcohol*, or *rectified spirits*.

Brandy in its pure state is colourless, and it obtains its yellow tint by extracting the colouring matter from the new casks in which it is kept. But if it should not have acquired the usual tinge in this way, it is coloured artificially, to give it the appearance of having been kept some time; it also undergoes as much *coopering* as rum, if not more, as its increased price is a greater temptation.

THE CUTLER

The Cutler makes knives, forks, razors, scissars, lancets, and all other sorts of cutting instruments. The chief art in this business consists in bringing the steel to a just temper, for which the following rules may be given.

Tempering consists in softening hardened steel by the application of a heat not greater than that which was employed in hardening it; for this purpose it is gradually heated more or less according to the temper required: and cooled again either gradually or rapidly, this making no difference; after which the steel is found to be softened or tempered exactly in proportion to the heat which it has undergone; while the steel is tempering, its surface displays a succession of colours (supposed to arise from a commencing oxydation) in proportion as it becomes more and more heated, which the workmen in this metal have ingeniously taken advantage of as serving to denominate the degree of temper required for different articles. The first perceptible colour is a light straw yellow, and this being produced by a small degree of heat, indicates the highest or hardest temper; to this succeeds a full yellow, then a brown, afterwards a reddish blue, then a light blue, and lastly a full deep blue passing into black, which being the other extremity of the series, denotes the lower degree of temper and a hardness only a little superior to what the piece of steel would have acquired if, when heated for the purpose of being hardened, it had been allowed to cool gradually instead of being plunged into a cold liquid. The old method of tempering, which is practised even yet by many manufacturers, is to lay the articles on a clear coal-fire, or on a hot bar till they exhibit the requisite colours; but small articles, which were to be reduced to a blue temper, were commonly *blazed,* that is, they were first dipped in oil, or melted grease, and then held over a fire till the oil became inflamed and thus evaporated. The following table shews the temperature at which the various colours make their appearence 430° to 450° the several tints of straw colour fit for razors, and such instruments as have a keen edge, and a stout back.

470° a full yellow, and proper for scalpels, pen knives, and other fine edged instruments.

490° the brown yellow, and a proper temperature for scissars and small shears. 510° the first tinge of purple, the proper temper for pocket and pruning knives. 530° indicates purple, the temper for table and carving knives. 550° to 560° the different shades of blue, a temper fit for watch springs, swords, and wherever great elasticity is required. 600° corresponds with black, and in the lowest degree of temperature — Aikin's Dictionary.

The principal places in this country for the manufactory of cutlery wares are Birmingham, Sheffield, Walsall, and Wolverhampton, at these towns goods of all kinds, in steel, are made much cheaper than in any other part of the world. In London the same goods bear a much higher price than those manufactured in the country, though the latter may be as good in quality, but perhaps not so neatly finished.

It is said, however, not to be very uncommon practice for London cutlers to fix their own names and marks on goods wrought at Birmingham, Sheffield, &c. by which means they can obtain for them more readily the price of town-made goods.

The blades of knives and forks are forged by fire; and after they are brought to the proper shape and size, they are polished, ground, and put into the handles.

The manufacture of skates is a considerable part of the cutler's business in severe winters: and in some of the principal shops swords are also mounted, but this does not properly belong to the cutler's profession. The sword-blades almost all come from abroad, where they are forged by large hammers moved by water-mills. In this manner the celebrated sword-blades of Solingen are made. Here the cutler is only concerned in mounting the blades, and in making the scabbards, the expence of which may be carried to almost any extent. It is no uncommon thing for a sword highly finished to be worth from 150 to 300 guineas; many of these have, within these few years, been presented to naval and military officers, by a society called the 'Patriotic Fund' who have associated for the express purpose of rewarding those heroes who have performed any great exploits in their country's service.

The manufacture of razors is another part of the cutler's business. As shaving to many people is a very painful operation, cutlers, in different countries, have long exerted all their skill to remove the inconvenience, but without that sort of success that may always be relied on. To whatever price we go for razors, we cannot depend upon their goodness; and it often happens that in a case of razors purchased at Sheffield, at a shilling a piece, one may find as many good ones as in a case bought in London at ten times the price.

The handles of knives are chiefly made of ivory, which is cut from the tusks or teeth of the elephant. They are brought to us from the East Indies, and from a particular part of Africa. They are valuable in proportion to their size. Ivory may be turned like wood, and it may, by a chemical process, be softened, worked to any particular form, and hardened again. There are methods also of colouring or staining ivory, so that we have red and green ivory as well as white.

The surgical instrument-maker is another species of cutler: he makes use of the best steel, and is supposed to be more careful in finishing, his instruments with a neater polish than the common cutler.

It has been recommended by a professional gentleman, to dip all surgical instruments in oil, previously to using, except the lancet intended for inoculation.

A journeyman cutler will, with ease, earn two guineas a week; those employed in the finer sorts of work much more. In all large shops one man is employed a certain number of days in each week in grinding old work; and this part of the business pays the master well.

THE MERCHANT

The merchant is a person who buys and sells almost every thing; and as merchandize includes all goods and wares exposed to sale in fairs or markets, so the name merchant formerly extended to every kind of traders. In France and Holland all buyers and sellers, whether in the wholesale or retail way, are called merchants. But in this country the term is appropriated to those who carry on commerce by importation and exportation, or by way of barter or exchange.

To carry on the business of a merchant with a high degree of credit a man should possess a large stock of general knowledge, and a considerable capital; the one will prevent him from falling into errors, and the other will enable him to give credit to his customers both at home and abroad.

The merchant should be perfectly acquainted with all the departments of writing, arithmetic, and the keeping of books, He should be expert in the forms of invoices, account of sales, policies of insurances, in the nature of charters, bills of lading, and bills of exchange. He should understand the agreement and difference which subsist between the monies, weights, and measures of different countries, or of different counties in his own country. He ought to have a general and accurate knowledge of all the different manufactures in which he deals, at least of the places where they are best made, and of the materials of which they are composed. He should know the best season for bringing his own goods to market, and be well acquainted with the nature of *exchange,* according to the course of different places, and with the causes of its rise and fall. He should know what merchandizes are permitted or prohibited, as well on entering as in going out of the kingdoms or states where they are manufactured. He should know the customs due on the importation or exportation of goods, according to the usage and regulations of the places to which he trades. He should understand the best methods of packing merchandizes, either to preserve them in warehouses or to adapt them for short or long voyages. He should know the price and condition of freighting and insuring ships and goods; and if the vessels, or any part of them, are his own property, he should be acquainted with their value; the expense of first building and subsequent repairs; the wages given to the several officers and sailors who work them, and the best method of engaging them in his service. He ought to be able to write letters with ease and elegance, and to understand as many foreign languages as he can. The following are, however, the most important for him to know: the *Spanish*, which is used not only in Spain, but on the coast of Africa, from the Canaries to the Cape of Good Hope; the *Italian,* which is understood on all the coasts of the Mediterranean, and in many parts of the Levant; the *German,* which is understood in almost all the northern countries; and the *French,* which is current in most parts of Europe. Finally, the merchant should be well acquainted with the laws, customs, and regulations of the countries to which he does or may trade.

Such are the branches of knowledge necessary to a person carrying on an extensive commerce, as a merchant to foreign parts; of course, any young man intended for that business should lay the foundation by a good education, and should be very diligent during the years which he spends as clerk, to prepare himself either for business of his own, or as a partner in a house already established.

The trade carried on by merchants in this country may be divided into *inland* and *foreign*. The inland trade consists in transporting the commodities of one part of the kingdom to another. The chief articles imported into London from other parts of the island are, corn, coals, hops, woollens, cottons, and linen; corn and hops are sold by persons called *factors.* Woollen goods are sent up by the clothiers, and sold by the factors of Blackwell hall. Linen cloth, from Ireland and Scotland, and printed cottons, &c. from Manchester, are consigned to the factors for those commodities.

The factors are a species of merchants who deal by commission, and sell the goods of other people consigned to them for a certain premium. Thus, a farmer in the country has a thousand quarters of wheat to sell at the London market; he cannot come conveniently to town, therefore he sends his wheat to a corn-factor, who sells it to the best advantage, receives the money, and remits it to the farmer, after having deducted his commission-money for trouble and expence.

There are also factors who deal in foreign commodities in the same manner. These are distinguished either by the countries they deal with, or by the goods usually assigned to them.

Merchants export the goods of his kingdom to the proper markets, and import the commodities of other countries in exchange. They are distinguished from one another either by the goods they traffic in, or by the countries with which they have their chief correspondence. Thus a merchant who deals chiefly in tobacco is called a tobacco-merchant; a dealer in wines is a wine-merchant.

West-India merchants export all manner of materials for wearing apparel, household furniture, cutlery, and haberdashery wares, watches, jewels, and toys, likewise some goods previously obtained from the East Indies, French wines, porter, linen cloths, &c; and our ships generally touch at Ireland and take in provisions. The returns from the West-India islands are, rum, coffee, sugar, cotton, indigo, mahogany, logwood, and other woods for dyeing.

From the states of North America our merchants import tobacco, rice, indigo, timber, hemp, flax, iron, pitch, tar, turpentine, sending in return the same articles as to the West-India islands.

From the East Indies and China they import tea, rice, drugs, colours, thrown, organzine or manufactured, and raw silk, salt-petre, cotton, shawls, muslins, calicoes, and some silken pieces, but the chief export to those countries is silver bullion, tin, lead, woollens, &c. and the ships touch at Madeira and the Cape of Good Hope, for wines on their way out.

Merchants have in their dealings much business with the *Custom-house,* which may be readily explained. Rum, sugar, and almost all articles imported from abroad, pay certain duties to government before they can be taken away: these duties are to be accounted for at the Custom house. Many articles manufactured here, as glass, leather, &c. pay very heavy taxes: now to encourage trade, these taxes, or part of them, are returned when the same articles are exported into foreign countries. These returns are called *drawbacks.* Merchants, therefore, or their clerks, must go to the Custom-house, and take oath as to the quantity and quality of goods exported, in order to obtain the customary draw-backs. Merchants are frequently ships owners.

Ships are also entered inwards and outwards, when they bring or proceed with cargoes, they also pay tonnage duty in this country on their arrival, the master is required to bring an account of his cargo to the custom house, which is called a manifest or report.

Bankers, though not properly merchants, are so connected with commerce as to claim notice here. A banker is a trustee to other people, and his house the repositary for their money. The business and gains of a banker may be thus described and explained:— A merchant, or gentleman, possessed of a large sum of money, not chusing to keep it in his own hands, places it for security in the custody of a banker, from whom he draws it at such times, and in such sums, as may suit his convenience. The banker, who is, or ought to be, a man of large property, knows that the several persons who have lodged money in his hands cannot have occasion for it at once; he therefore lends out upon good security, such sums as he thinks he can spare from his current demands; and from these loans, upon which he receives 5 per cent, arise his profits.

The banker deals also in *exchange,* that is, in remitting money from one place to another. If, for instance, I owe a man in Holland a thousand guilders, which I have promised to pay at certain period, I must apply to a banker, to whom I pay the guilders, or their equivalent in pounds sterling, and he gives me a draft for the same sum upon his correspondent in Holland, which I remit to my creditor.

Insurers, or *Underwriters,* are a species of merchants who insure goods from one port to another for a certain premium. If I have a ship bound with goods for the East Indies, there is a risk of its being lost at sea, or, in time of war, of being taken by an enemy; I therefore go to an under-writer and pay him 5 per cent. more or less, upon condition that he pay me as many hundred pounds as I have insured in case the vessel should be lost, or captured by the enemy.

THE BRICK-MAKER

The business of a brickmaker is carried on in the open fields, and its mode of operation may be seen in the neighbourhood of most large towns. The art in almost all its branches is regulated by different acts of parliament: and bricks may be made of pure clay, or of clay mixed, in certain proportions, with sand or ashes.

The clay is first moistened and tempered with water, either by the hand, or by means of a machine or mill worked with one or more horses. When it is fit for moulding into bricks, several persons are usually, in the neighbourhood of London, employed upon the business of making a single brick; these are called a gang: they consist of one or two men, a woman, and two children, to each of which is assigned a different department in the occupation. A gang in full work will make many thousand bricks in the course of a single week.

The man moulding the clay into the shape of a brick stands under a sort of thatched cover to keep off the sun and the rain: on a board before him are all his implements; the mould into which the clay is put, the clay itself, which is brought to him by another person, a vessel with some water, and a little heap of sand; and near lies the ruler with which he takes off the superfluous clay from the mould.

The inside of the box or mould is exactly the shape and size of a brick: the workman throws the clay into this with some violence, having first scattered a little sand about the sides of it; and then scraping off the superfluous clay, he lifts up the mould, and between two small boards conveys it to the barrow which stands near him on the ground. When the barrow is loaded another person comes and wheels away the bricks, and piles them up in an open place to dry. When the pile is made of the proper height, he covers them with long straw, so that they may dry gradually without being exposed to the direct rays of the sun, which would crack them. Heavy rains would also be injurious to them; these are likewise kept off by the straw. As soon as they are sufficiently dry for the purpose they are to be burnt in a kiln. Here great art is required in piling the bricks, so that the fire may circulate through every course and in all directions. Breeze, that is small cinders from sea-coal, is the fuel used in burning bricks, and when once well lighted it will keep burning several days till the bricks are completely finished.

Bricks when finished are of different colours, according to the clay of which they are made, but they must be all of one size; namely, nine inches long, four inches broad, and two inches and a half thick. A duty of 5s.10d is charged upon every thousand of common bricks; of course this business affords a large revenue to government.

The most beautiful white bricks made in this country are manufactured at Woolpit in Suffolk; these are brought by means of water-carriage to all parts of England where great neatness in brick-work is an object.

Stourbridge clay and Windsor loam are esteemed the best for making bricks that are required to bear a very intense heat. These are used for coating furnaces, and lining the ovens of glass-houses, where they stand the utmost fury of the fire.

A gang of brick-makers will earn a handsome living: sometimes it happens that the whole gang consists of branches of the same family, as the father and mother, and four or five children of different ages; these will earn from two to three guineas a week; but they work many hours, and their labour is very hard.

In connection with the trade of brick-making we must notice the manufacture of tiles, which is a sort of thin brick, made use of in the roofs of houses, and also, when something thicker, for the purposes of paving. Those for covering the roofs of houses are of different shapes, according to the uses for which they are intended; these are plain tiles, ridge-tiles, gutter-tiles, pan tiles, &c. They are all made according to certain gauges; and the makers are subject to heavy penalties if their tiles exceed the dimensions fixed on by the several acts of parliament. The kilns in which tiles are burnt are large conical buildings: in these the tiles are piled from the bottom to the top before the fire is lighted. A very large manufactory of this sort is situated near Bagnigge Wells.

Dutch clinkers are imported into England for the purpose of paving; they are long narrow bricks of a brimstone colour, very hard and well burnt, so as to be nearly vitrified.

Flemish or Dutch tiles, which are glazed and painted, were formerly much used in chimney-jaumbs. Some thirty or forty years ago it was not uncommon to see a complete scripture history, and other curious devices, in a parlour fire-place.

THE ROPE-MAKER

Rope-making is an art of very great importance; for without the assistance of string, cords, ropes, cables, &c. a very small part of the business of life could be carried on that is now transacted.

Ropes of all kinds are made of hemp, twisted or spun something after the same manner of spinning wool; and the places in which ropes are manufactured are called rope-walks. These are a quarter of a mile or more in length, in the open air, but usually covered over with a slight shed to keep the workmen from the inclemencies and changes of the weather.

At the upper-end of the rope-walk is a spinning-wheel, which is turned round by a person who sits on a stool or bench for the purpose: the man who forms the rope or string has a bundle of dressed hemp, round his waist. From this he draws out two or more ends and fixes them to a hook: the wheel is now turned by which the threads are twisted, and as the spinner walks backward the rope, or more properly the rope-yarn, is lengthened. The part already twisted draws along with it more fibres out of the bundle, and the spinner gives assistance to it with his fingers, supplying hemp in due proportion as he walks away from the wheel, and taking care that the fibres come in equally from both sides of his bundle, and that they enter always with their ends, and not by the middle, which would double them. The arrangement of the fibres and the degree of twisting depend on the skill and dexterity of the spinner. The degree of twist depends on the rate of the wheel's motion, combined with the retrograde motion of the spinner.

As soon as he is arrived at the lower end of the walk, he calls out, and another spinner immediately detaches the yarn from the hook of the wheel, gives it to a third person, who takes it to the reel, and the second spinner attaches his own hemp to the whirlhook. In the mean time the first spinner keeps fast hold of the end of his yarn, to prevent its untwisting and as soon as the reeler begins to turn his reel, he goes slowly up the walks, keeping the yarn of an equal tightness all the way, till he arrives at the wheel, where he waits with his yarn in hand till another has finished his yarn. The first spinner takes it off the whirl-hook, joins it to his own, that it may follow it on the reel, and begins a new yarn himself.

The fibres of hemp are thus twisted into yarns, and make a line of any length: down the rope-walk are a number of upright posts with long pegs fixed in them at right angles; on these pegs the spinner throws the rope-yarn as he proceeds, to prevent its swagging.

As many fibres are made into one yarn, so many yarns are afterward made into one rope, according to the size and strength required. By this process, which is called *laying*, it acquires a solidity and hardness which render it less penetrable by water, that would rot it in a short time.

Sometimes the union of several yarns is called a strand, and a larger rope may be formed of two or more of these strands: and in this manner cables and other ground tackle are commonly made.

Cables and cords are frequently tarred, which is usually done in the state of yarn, this being the only method that the hemp can be uniformly penetrated. The yarn is made to wind off from one reel, and having passed through a vessel containing hot tar, it is wound upon another, and the superfluous tar is taken off by passing through a hole surrounded with spungy oakum; or it is sometimes tarred in skains or hauls, which are drawn by a capstan through the tar-kettle, and through a hole formed of two plates of metal.

It is a fact, however, that tarred cordage is very much weaker than white, it is also less pliable and less durable; but the use of tar is nevertheless necessary to defend the cordage from the action of the water.

Nets are made with small cords; large ones are used for tying up packages; and ropes of all sizes and dimensions are used for shipping. A ship's cable is sometimes several hundred yards in length, and is worth a large sum of money.

The master rope-maker requires a considerable capital if his business is carried on upon a large scale, and a journeyman will earn with ease from a guinea to a guinea and a half a week, or even more if he is sober and industrious.

Yarn for sail-cloth is made of dressed hemp, and spun in the same manner that rope-yarn is spun. The spinner of this may make a good living; women are chiefly employed in it. The person who shapes and sews together the cloth into sails is called a sail-maker, and is sometimes denominated a ship's taylor.

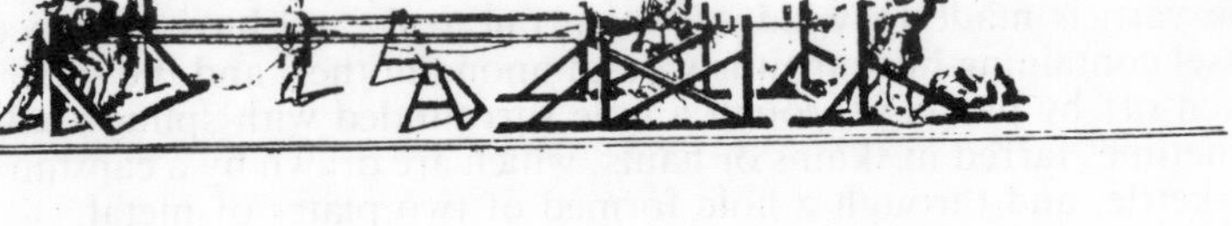

THE WEAVER

Weaving is a very extensive trade, and is divided into a number of different branches, such as the broad and narrow weavers. The broad weaver is employed in stuffs, broad-cloths, woollen goods, &c.: the narrow weaver, in ribbons, tapes, and such other things: and there are engine looms for making some of these narrow goods, by which ten or twelve pieces can be made at once: but goods made in this way are generally not so good as those made by hand, because it is not possible to find thread in every part equal; but the engines give an equal pressure upon all threads, while the workman, weaving by hand, increases or diminishes the strength of his pull according to the quality of the thread, and by that method conceals all difference in the warp.

Linen and woollen cloth are both woven the same way; the one from thread, the other from worsted. So also is silk, which, when taken from the silk-worm, and wound, is called floss silk, and afterwards spun into sewing-silk.

The weaver sits at his *loom;* this is a machine by which several distinct threads of any kind are woven into one piece. They are of various structures, according to the several kinds of materials to be woven and to the methods of weaving them. The other principal things to be noticed are the *warp,* the *woof,* and the *shuttle.*

The warp is the threads, whether of silk, wool, linen, or cotton, that are extended lengthwise on the loom.

The *woof* is the thread which the weaver shoots across the warp, by means of a little instrument called a *shuttle.*

The *shuttle* serves to form the woof by being thrown alternately from right to left, and from left to right, across and between the threads of the warp. In the middle of the shuttle is a cavity called the eye or chamber, and in this is enclosed the spole or bobbin, on which the thread or part of it is wound.

The ribbon-weaver's shuttle is different from that of most other weavers, though it serves for the same purpose. It is made of box, and is six or seven inches long, shod with iron at both ends, which terminate in points that are crooked, one towards the right, the other towards the left.

The weaver has a reel, by means of which the thread is wound on bobbins that lie in a wooden bowl. The thread for the warp is wound on a kind of large wooden bobbins to dispose it for warping.

When the warp is mounted, the weaver treads alternately on the treddle, first on the right step, and then on the left, which raises and lowers the threads of the warp equally; between these he throws transversely the shuttle from the one to the other: and every time that the shuttle is thus thrown a thread of the woof is inserted in the warp. In this manner the work is continued till the piece is finished, that is, till the whole warp is filled with the woof, it is then taken off the loom by unrolling it from the beam on which it had been rolled, in proportion as it was wove,

To give woollen stuff the necessary qualities, it is required that the thread of the warp be of the same kind of wool, and of the same fineness throughout.

The woof is of different matter, according to the piece to be made. In taffety, both woof and warp are of silk. In mohairs, the woof is usually flax, and the warp silk. In satins the warp is frequently wool, and the woof silk.

The common weaver requires but little ingenuity in carrying on his business, but weavers of flowered silks, damask, velvets, &c. ought to be people possessed of a considerable capacity: it is an advantage to them if they are able to draw and design their own patterns.

Journeymen weavers can, while in constant employ, make a good living; they will earn a guinea and a half or two guineas a week, according to the substance on which they are employed. It is a business that requires no great degree of strength, and a lad may be bound apprentice to it at twelve or thirteen years of age. Among weavers are frequently found men of a thoughtful and literary turn. One of the first mathematicians of this country was Mr. Thomas Simpson, an industrious weaver in Spitalfields.

The silk-throwster prepares by means of a mill the raw silk for the use of the weaver: he employs women chiefly. Spinning the hard silk and winding it employ a great number of hands of almost all ages.

THE STOCKING-WEAVER

Formerly stockings were made of cloths, or of milled stuffs sewed to gether; but since the invention of knitting and weaving stockings of silk, wool, cotton, thread, &c. the use of cloth stockings has been entirely discontinued. In the year 1561, queen Elizabeth was presented with a pair of black knit silk stockings, with which she was so much pleased as to discontinue the use of those made with cloth. It is said also by Dr. Howel, in his History of the World, that Henry VIII commonly wore cloth hose, except by accident he obtained a pair of silk stockings. His son Edward the Sixth was presented with a pair of long Spanish silk stockings by Sir Thoms Gresham, and the donation was highly esteemed. From these accounts, it should seem that the invention of knit silk stockings originally came from Spain.

William Rider was the first person who made them in England: and he, it is said, learnt the art at the house of an Italian merchant, and knit a pair of worsted stockings, which he presented to William earl of Pembroke in the year 1564.

Modern stockings, whether woven or knit, are formed of an indefinite number of little knots, called stitches, loops, or meshes, intermingled in one another.

Woven stockings are manufactured on a machine made of finely-polished iron or steel. It is of a structure too complex to admit of a description in this little work.

The invention of this machine is ascribed to William Lee, M.A. of St.John's-College, Cambridge, in the year 1589. But by other persons the credit of it is given to a student of Oxford, who was driven to pursuits of industry through mere necessity. This young man, falling in love with an inn-keeper's daughter, married her, though she had not a penny, and he, by his marriage, lost his fellowship. They soon became miserably poor, and the only means by which they could support themselves were the knitting of stockings, at which the woman was very expert. Sitting constantly together from morning to night, the young man observed with great attention the motion of his wife's fingers in the dexterous management of her needles, and conceived that it was possible to contrive a little loom which might perform the work with more expedition. They soon began to make the experiment, which completely succeeded. Thus the stocking-loom was first invented; by which the inventor not only placed himself above want, but has rendered to his country great and important benefits, stockings being a considerable article for exportation from this to foreign countries.

The loom of course received several improvements, so that at length stockings of all sorts can be made on it with great art and expedition. By means of some additional machinery to the stocking-frame, the turned ribbed stockings are made as well as those done with knitting-needles. These, together with the manner of making the open-work mills, a curious sort of lace, aprons, and handkerchiefs, as well as a great variety of figured goods for waistcoats, &c. have sprung from the same machine, and form now a considerable additional branch of the stocking-trade.

Knit stockings are made with needles of polished iron, which inter-weave the thread, and form the meshes of which the stockings consist. This part of the invention, as it is now practised, is given by some to Scotland, by others to France, though it probably originated in Spain. In Paris there is no great house without its porter, and these porters employ all their leisure moments in the knitting of stockings. In England knitting is not much carried on as a trade, but in country places most female servants are expected to be able to fill up their time in this way.

Knit stockings are much more durable than those made in the loom; but the time required for this work, especially if the materials are very fine, raises the price too high for common wearers. The Scotch are said to make the best knit stockings of any people in Europe, and they sell at enormously high prices, from thirty shillings to four or five pounds a pair.

The stocking-weaver requires more genius than strength. It is a profitable business to the master, but journeymen must have considerable application to earn more than a guinea and a half a week. It is, however, clean neat work, and unexposed to the inclemencies of the weather. They are paid so much for each pair of stockings, and the price varies according to the fineness of the thread, cotton, silk or worsted, of which they are manufactured: if however the workmen do not possess a loom of their own, they allow the master two shillings a week for the use of his. Looms will cost from fifty to a hundred and fifty guineas each.

The hosier purchases stockings, night-caps, socks, gloves, &c. from the manufacturer, and sells them again. Some of them employ looms, and are in that respect stocking-weavers. The business of the hosier consists in being able properly to appreciate the value of the goods in which he deals, an art which is easily acquired, and which ought to be reserved for the female sex, for whom, unfortunately, there are not a sufficient number of occupations appropriated.

CARPET-WEAVER

The carpet-loom consists principally of four pieces, two long planks or cheeks of wood, and two thick rollers or beams. The planks are set upright, and the rollers across, the one at the top and the other at bottom, about a foot or more distant from the ground. They are suspended on the planks, and may be turned with bars. In each roller is a groove from one end to the other, in which the ends of the warp are so fastened that all the threads of its are kept perpendicular.

The warp is divided both before and behind into parcels of ten threads through the whole width of the piece. The weaver works on the foreside. The design or pattern is traced in its proper colours on cartons, tied about the workman, who looks at it every moment, because every stich is marked upon it, which it is his business to imitate. By this means he always knows what colours and shades he is to use, and how many stitches of the same colour. To accomplish this, he is assisted by squares, into which the whole design is divided; each square is subdivided into ten vertical lines, corresponding with the parcels of ten threads of the warp; and besides, each square is ruled with ten horizontal lines, crossing the vertical lines at right angles. The workman, having placed his spindles of thread near him, begins to work on the first horizontal line of one of the squares.

The lines marked on the carton are not traced on the warp, because an iron wire, which is longer than the width of a parcel of ten threads, supplies the place of a cross line. This wire is managed by a crook at one end, at the workman's right hand; towards the other end it is flatted into a sort of knife, with a back and edge, and grows wider to the point. The weaver fixes his iron wire horizontally on the warp, by twisting some turns of a suitable thread of the woof round it, which he passes forward and backwards, behind a fore thread of the warp, and then behind the opposite thread, drawing them in their turn by their leishes. Afterwards, he brings the woof-thread round the wire, in order to begin again to thrust it into the warp. He continues in this manner to cover the iron rod or wire, and to fill up a line to the tenth thread of the warp. He is at liberty either to stop here, or to go on with the same cross line in the next division, according as he passes the thread of the woof round the iron wire, and into the warp, the thread of which he causes to cross one another at every instant: when he comes to the end of the line, he takes care to strike in, or close again all the stitches with an iron reed, the teeth of which freely enter between the empty threads of the warp, and which is heavy enough to strike in the woof he has used. This row of stitches is again closed and levelled, and in the same manner the weaver proceeds; then with his left hand he lays a strong pair of sheers along the finished line, cuts off the loose hairs, and thus forms a row of tufts perfectly even, which, together with those before and after it, form the shag. Thus the workman follows stitch for stitch, and colour for colour, the plan of his pattern, which he is attempting to imitate; he paints magnificently, without having the least notion of painting or drawing.

The manufacture of carpets, after the manner of Chaillot, was introduced into London in the year 1750, by two workmen who left the manufactory in disgust, and came here to procure employment. They were first encouraged by Mr. Moore, who succeeded in establishing this important and useful manufacture, and who in the year 1757 obtained a premium from the Society of Arts for the best carpet in imitation of the Turkey carpets. We have carpet manufactories at Axminster, Wilton, Kidderminster, Leeds, and many other places. It is a good business for the masters and journeymen, and now carpets are become of such general use, a great number of people are employed in the manufacture.

Axminster carpets are manufactured of any size: they are woven in one entire piece, and several persons are employed at the same time in working the coloured patterns.

Another sort of carpet in use, is made of narrow slips of list sewed together; these of course are very inferior to those just described, but they employ many women and children. A considerable trade in the list carpets is carried on at the Orphan Working School in the City-road, an institution that does honour to the liberality and public spirit of the Dissenters in and near the metropolis.

THE LADIES' DRESS-MAKER

The business of a mantua-maker, which now includes almost every article of dress made use of by ladies, except, perhaps, those which belong to the head and the feet, is too well known to stand in need of description.

The mantua-maker takes the pattern off from a lady by means of a piece of paper, or of cloth. The pattern, if taken in cloth, become afterwards the lining of the dress. This business requires, in those who would excel in it, a considerable share of taste, but no great capital to carry it on, unless to the act of making is united the business of furnishing the materials.

The mantua-maker's customers are not always easily pleased: they frequently expect more from their dress than it is capable of giving. "Dress," says Mr. Addison, "is grown of universal use in the conduct of life. Civilities and respect are only paid to appearance. It is a varnish that give a lustre to every action, that introduces us into all polite assemblies, and the only certain method of making most of the youth of our nation conspicuous: hence Milton asserts of the fair sex,

-------------------of outward form
Elaborate, of inward less exact.

"A lady of genius will give a genteel air to her whole dress by a well fancied suit of knots, as a judicious writer gives a spirit to a whole sentence by a single expression. As words grow old, and new ones enrich the language, so there is a constant succession of dress; the fringe succeeds the lace; the stays shorten or extend the waist; the ribbon undergoes divers variations; the head-dress receives frequent rises and falls every year; and, in short, the whole woman throughout, as curious observers of dress have remarked, is changed from top to toe in the period of five years.

"The mantua-maker, must be an expert anatomist; and must, if judiciously chosen, have a name of French termination: she must know how to hide all defects in the proportions of the body, and must be able to mould the shape by the stays, that while she corrects the body she may not interfere with the pleasures of the palate."

It will therefore be readily admitted, that the perfection of dress, and the art of pleasing the fair sex in this particular cannot be attained without a genius: the indignation expressed against those who fail in the pretensions is referred to by Pope:

Not Cynthia, when her *mantua's* pinn'd awry,
E'er felt such rage, resentment, and despair,
As thou, sad virgin! for thy ravish'd hair.

The business of a mantua-maker, when conducted upon a large scale and in a fashionable situation, is very profitable; but the mere work-women do not make gains at all adequate to their labour; they are frequently obliged to sit up to very late hours, and the recompense for extra-work is in general a poor remuneration for the time spent. Young women ought, perhaps, rarely to be apprenticed to this trade unless their friends can, at the end of the term, place them in a reputable way of business, and can command such connections as shall, with industry, secure their success. The price charged for making dresses cannot be estimated: it varies with the article to be made; with the reputation of the maker; with her situation in life; and even with the season of the year.

Mantua-makers work in silks, muslins, cambrics, cottons, and a great variety of articles, adapted as well to please the fancy as for purposes of real utility. They require but few implements: these are chiefly thread, scissars (sic), pins, and needles.

Muslin is a fine sort of cloth, wholly made of cotton, so named from the circumstance of having a downy nap on its surface, resembling *moss*, which in French is called *mousse*. Muslins come from the East Indies.

Cambric is a species of linen made of flax, very fine and white; it derives its name from Cambray in France, where it was first manufactured.

THE PIN-MAKER

There is scarcely any commodity cheaper than pins, and but few that pass through more hands before they come to be sold. It is reckoned that twenty-five workmen are successively employed in each pin, between the drawing of the brass wire and the sticking of the pin in the paper.

It is not easy to trace the invention of this very useful little implement: it is first noticed in the English statute book in the year 1483, prohibiting foreign manufactures: and it appears from the manner in which pins are described in the reign of Henry the Eighth, and the labour and time which the manufacture of them would require, that they were a new invention in this country, and probably brought from France.

At this period pins were considered in Paris as articles of luxury: and no master pin-maker was allowed to open more than one shop for the sale of his wares, except on New-year's day, and the day before that: it should seem, therefore, that pins were given away as new-year's gifts; hence arose the phrase pin-money, the name of an allowance frequently made by the husband to his wife for her own spending.

Pins are now made wholly of brass wire; formerly iron wire was made use of, but the ill effects of iron have nearly discarded that substance from the pin-manufactory. The excellence and perfection of pins consist in the stiffness of the wire, and its blanching; in the heads being well turned, and the points accurately filed. The following are some of the principal operations.

When the brass wire, of which the pins are formed, is first received, it is generally too thick for the purpose of being cut into pins. It is therefore wound off from one wheel to another, with great velocity, and made to pass between the two, through a circle in a piece of iron of smaller diameter. The wire is then straightened, and afterwards cut into lengths of three or four yards, and then into smaller ones, every length being sufficient to make six pins; each end of these is ground to a point, which is performed by a boy, who sets with two small grinding-stones before him, turned by a wheel. Taking up a handful, he applies the ends to the coarsest of the two stones, being careful at the same time to keep each piece moving round between his fingers, so that the points may not become flat: he then gives them to the other stone; and by that means a lad of twelve or fourteen years of age is enabled to point about 16,000 pins in an hour. When the wire is thus pointed, a pin is taken off from each end, and this is repeated till it is cut into six pieces. The next operation is that of forming the heads, or, as they term it, *head-spinning;* which is done by means of a spinning-wheel, one piece of wire being thus wound round another with astonishing rapidity, and the interior one being drawn out, leaves a hollow tube; it is then cut with shears, every two turns of the wire forming one head; these are softened by throwing them into iron pans, and placing them in a furnace till they are red-hot. As soon as they are cool, they are distributed to children, who sit with their anvils and hammers before them, which they work with their feet, by means of a lathe; and taking up one of the lengths, they thrust the blunt end into a quantity of the heads that lie before them, and catching one at the extremity, they apply them immediately to the anvil and hammer, and by a motion or two of the foot, the point and the head are fixed together in much less time than it can be described in, and with a dexterity only to be acquired by practice, the spectator being in continual apprehension for the safety of their fingers' ends.

The pin is now finished as to its form, but still it is merely brass; for which purpose it is thrown into a copper containing a solution of tin and the leys of wine. Here it remains for some time; and when taken out it assumes a white though dull appearance. To give it a polish, it is put into a tub containing a quantity of bran, which is set in motion by turning a shaft that runs through its centre, and thus by means of friction it becomes perfectly bright. The pin being complete, nothing remains but to separate it from the bran, which is performed by a mode exactly similar to the winnowing of corn, the bran flying off, and leaving the pins behind for immediate sale.

The pins most esteemed in commerce are those of England; those of Bourdeaux are next; then those made in some of the other departments of France. The London pointing and blanching are most in repute, because our pin-makers, in pointing, use two steel-mills, the first of which turns the point, and the latter takes off all irregularities, and renders it smooth, and, as it were, polished; and in blanching they use block-tin, granulated; whereas in other places they mix their tin with lead and quicksilver, which not only blanches worse than the former, but is also dangerous, as any puncture made with pins of this sort is not so readily cured.

Pins are distinguished by numbers; the smaller are called from No. 3,4, 5, to the 14th whence they go by *twos,* viz. No. 16, 18, and 20, which is the largest size. Besides the white pins, there are black ones, made for the use of mourning, from No. 4 to No. 10. There are pins with double heads of several numbers, used by ladies to fix the buckles of their hair for the night, without the danger of pricking.

THE NEEDLE-MAKER

We shall now give a short account of the manufacture of needles: these make a very considerable article in commerce, the consumption of them is almost incredible. The sizes are from No. 1, the largest, to No. 25, the smallest. In the manufacture of needles, the German and Hungarian steel are of the most repute.

The first thing in making needles is, to pass the steel through a coal fire, and by means of a hammer to bring it into a cylindrical form. This being done, it is drawn through a large hole of a wire-drawing iron, and returned into the fire and drawn through a second hole of the iron smaller than the first, and so on till it has acquired the degree of fineness required for that species of needles. The steel, thus reduced to a fine wire, is cut in pieces of the length of the needles intended. These pieces are flatted at one end on the anvil, in order to form the head and eye. They are then softened and pierced at each extreme of the flat part, on the anvil, by a punch of well-tempered steel, and laid on a leaden block to bring out, with another punch, the little piece of steel remaining in the eye. When the head and eye are finished, the point is formed with a file, and the whole filed over: they are then laid to heat red hot on a long narrow iron, crooked at one end, in a charcoal fire: and when taken out from thence, they are thrown into a bason of cold water to harden. They are next placed in an iron shovel on a fire more or less brisk in proportion to the thickness of the needles, taking care to move them from time to time. This serves to temper them, and take off their brittleness. They are now to be straightened one after another with the hammer.

The next process is the polishing. To do this they take twelve or fifteen thousand needles, and range them in little heaps against each other on a piece of new buckram sprinkled with emery-dust. The needles being thus disposed, emery-dust is thrown over them, which is again sprinkled with oil of olives; at last the whole is made up into a roll, well bound at both ends. This roll is laid on a polishing-table, and over it a thick plank loaded with stones, which men work backwards and forwards for two days successively, by these means the needles become insensibly polished. They are now taken out, and the filth washed off with hot water and soap; they are then wiped in hot bran, a little moistened, placed with the needles in a round box, suspended in the air by a cord, which is kept stirring till the bran and needles are dry. The needles are now sorted; the points are turned the same way, and smoothed with a emery-stone turned with a wheel; this is the end of the process, and nothing remains to be done but to make them up in packets of 250 each.

Needles were first made in England, by a native of India, in 1545, but the art was lost at his death: it was, however, shortly after recovered by Christopher Greening, who, with his three chidlren, were settled by Dr. Damer, ancestors of the present Lord Milton, at Long Crendon, in Bucks, where the manufactory has been carried on from that time to the present.

THE WIRE-DRAWER

Metal wires are frequently drawn so fine as to be wrought with other threads, of silk, wool, or hemp; and thus they become a considerable article in the manufactures. The metals most commonly drawn into wire are gold, silver, copper, and iron.

Silver wire and gold wire are the same, except that the latter is covered with gold. There are also counterfeit gold and silver wires, made of copper gilt and silvered over.

The business of a wire-drawer is thus performed: if it is gold wire that is wanted, an ingot of silver is double gilt, and then by the assistance of a mill it is drawn into wire. The mill consists of a steel plate, perforated with holes of different dimensions, and a wheel which turns the spindles. The ingot, which at first is but small, is passed through the largest hole, and then through one a degree smaller, and so continued till it is drawn to the required fineness; and it is all equally gilt, if drawn out as fine as a hair.

The next operation is that of the *flatting-mill,* which consists of two perfectly round and exquisitely polished rollers, formed internally of iron, and welded over with a plate of refined steel; these rollers are placed with their axes parallel and their circumferences nearly in contact, they are both turned with one handle: the lowermost is about ten inches in diameter, the upper about two, and they are something more than an inch in thickness. The wire unwinding from a bobbin, and passing between the leaves of a book gently pressed, and through a narrow slit in an upright piece of wood, called a ketch, is directed by a small conical hole in a piece of iron called a guide, to any particular part of the width of the rollers, some of which are capable of receiving, by this contrivance, forty threads. When the wire is flatted between the rollers, it is wound again on a bobbin, which is turned by a wheel, fixed on the axis of one of the rollers, and so proportioned, that the motion of the bobbin just keeps pace with that of the rollers.

Brass and copper wire is drawn in a similar manner to that already described. Of the brass wire there are many different sizes, suited to different kinds of works. The finest is used for the strings of musical instruments. Pin-makers also use great quantities of wires of several sizes to make pins of.

Iron wire is made from bars of iron, which are first drawn out to a greater length, to about the thickness of half an inch in diameter, at a furnace with a hammer gently moved by water. These thinner pieces are bored round, and put into a furnace to anneal. A very strong fire is necessary for this operation.

They are then delivered to the workmen called rippers, who draw them into wire through two or three holes, and then annealed a second time: after which they are to be drawn into wire of the thickness of a packthread after this they are again to be annealed, and then delivered to the small-wire-drawers. The plate, in which the holes are, is iron on the outside, and the wire is anointed with oil, to make it run the easier. The first iron that runs from the stone, when melting, being the softest and toughest, is usually preserved to make wire of.

It is difficult to determine the period when attempts were originally made to draw into threads metal cut or beat into small slips, by forcing them through holes in a steel plate. It should appear that as long as the work was performed by the hammer, the artists at Nuremberg were called *wire-smiths;* but after the invention of drawing iron, they were denominated wire-*drawers*. or wire-*millers*. Both these appellations occur in history so early as the year 1351; therefore the invention must have been known in the fourteenth century.

At first, threads exceedingly massy were employed for weaving and embroidery: it is not at all known when the *flatted* metal wire began to be spun round linen or silk thread. The spinning-mill, by which the labour is now performed, is a contrivance of great ingenuity.

The wire first spun about thread was round; and the invention of previously making the wire flat is probably a new epoch in the history of the art: and it is a curious fact, that three times as much silk can be covered by flatted as by round wire; so that various ornamental articles are cheap in the same proportion. Besides, the brightness of the metal is heightened in an uncommon degree, and the article becomes much more beautiful.

The greatest improvement ever made in this art, was undoubtedly the invention of the large drawing-machine, which is driven by water or by steam, and in which the axle-tree, by means of a lever, moves a pair of pincers, that open as they fall against the drawing-plate; lay hold of the wire, which is guided through a hole of the plate; shut as they are drawn back; and in that manner pull the wire along with them.

Wire-drawing, in all its branches, is profitable to the master, and to the workman it is a good business, being a trade that is not exposed to the weather, that can be carried on at all seasons of the year, and by which he may earn from one guinea to double that sum in a week.

THE PAPER-MAKER

The manufacture of paper is so curious, and so well worth the attention of young persons, that we recommend them to take some pains to get a sight of the whole process, which may easily be done wherever there are paper-mills.

Linen, such as our shirts is made of, is spun from flax that grows in the fields; and from linen rags, that is, from shirts and other articles of dress, when worn thread-bare, fine white paper is manufactured: of course every piece of rag, however small, should be preserved, and not thrown into the fire.

The first thing to be done towards the formation of paper, is to put the rags into a machine, or cylinder, formed of wire, which is made to turn round with great velocity to whirl out the dust; they are then sorted according to their different qualities; after which they are put into a large cistern or trough perforated with holes, through which a stream of clear water constantly flows. In this cistern is placed a cylinder about two feet long, set thick with rows of iron spikes. At the bottom of the trough there are corresponding rows of spikes. The cylinder is made to whirl round with inconceivable rapidity, and, with the iron teeth, rends and tears the cloth to atoms, till with the assistance of the water it is reduced to a thin pulp. By the same process all the impurities are cleared away, and it is restored to its original whiteness. This fine pulp is next put into a copper of warm water, and here it become the substance of paper, and ready for the mould; for which purpose it is conveyed to the vat. The vat is made of wood, generally about five feet broad, and two or three feet in depth. It is kept to a proper temperature by means of a charcoal fire.

The mould is composed of many wires set in a frame close together, and of another moveable frame equal in size to the sheet of paper to be made. These wires are disposed in the shape of the figure, which is discovered in a sheet of paper when we hold it up to the light.

The workman holds the frame in both his hands, plunges it horizontally into the tub, and takes it up quickly; the water runs away between the wires, and there remains nothing on the mould but the beaten pulp, in a thin coat, which forms the sheet of paper.

Another person, called the *coucher,* receives the mould, and places the sheet of paper on a felt or woollen cloth, during which the workman makes another sheet. They proceed in this manner, laying alternately a sheet and a felt, till they have made six quires of paper, which are called a post. When the last sheet of the post is covered with the last felt, the workman employed about the vat unite, and submit the whole heap to the action of the press. After this operation, another person separates the sheets of paper from the felts, laying them in a heap; and several of these heaps collected together are again put under the press. They are turned and pressed several times, and then the sheets are hung up, three or four together, on lines to dry.

The paper is now to be *sized,* because in its present state it will not bear the ink. The size is made of shreds and parings, collected from the tanners, curriers, and parchment-makers: and immediately before the operation, a certain quantity of alum is added to the size. The workman then takes a handful of the sheets, smoothed and rendered as supple as possible, and dips them into the vessel containing the size, and when he has finished ten or a dozen of these handfuls, they are submitted to the action of the press; the superflous size is carried back to the vessel by means of a small pipe. The paper is now to be hung, sheet by sheet, on lines to dry.

When the paper is sufficiently dry, it is carried to the finishing-room where it is pressed, selected, examined, folded, made up into quires, and finally into reams. It is here submitted twice to the press; first, when it is at its full size, and secondly, after it is folded.

Every quire of paper consists of twenty-four or twenty-five sheets; that is, the larger number refers to paper made use of in printing: and each ream contains twenty quires.

In the manufacture many sheets are damaged; these, in the sorting-room, are put together, and two of the worst quires are placed on the outsides of the ream, called *outside* quires. The reams are tied up in wrappers made of the settling of the vat, and then they are fit for sale. Some paper is made smooth and glossy like satin, by means of hot plates; this is called hot-pressing. The process of paper-making takes about three weeks.

Paste-board is made in a similar way to that of paper.

Blotting-paper, and paper used for filtering fluids, is paper not sized, in which therefore the ink readily sinks or spreads. Brown and other coloured papers are made of coarse or coloured rags.

Wove or woven paper is made in moulds, the wires of which are exceedingly fine, or equal thickness, and woven or laticed one within another. The marks, therefore, of these are easily pressed out, so as to be scarcely visible.

THE PRINTER

There are three kinds of printing: one from copper-plates, for pictures, another from moveable letters for books, which is the subject of the present article; and the third from blocks, for printing calicoes, linens, cottons, &c.

Of these branches, that of letter-press printing is the most curious, and the most important to the interests of mankind; since to this art we are indebted for our deliverance from ignorance and error, for the progress of learning, the revival of the sciences, and numberless improvements in the arts, which would have either been lost to mankind, or confined to the knowledge of a few persons only. "To the art of printing," says Dr. Knox, "we owe the Reformation. If the books of Luther had been multiplied only by the slow process of the hand-writing, they must have been few, and would have easily been suppressed by the combination of wealth and power; but poured forth in abundance from the press, they spread over the land with the rapidity of an inundation, which acquires additional force from the efforts used to obstruct its progress. He who undertook to prevent the dispersion of books once issued from the press, attempted a task no less arduous than the destruction of the hydra. Resistance was in vain, and religion was reformed; and we who are chiefly interested in this happy revolution must remember, amidst the praises bestowed on Luther, that his endeavours would have been ineffectual, unassisted by the invention of printing."

The art of printing, in whatever light it is viewed, claims the highest respect and attention. From the ingenuity of the contrivance, it has ever excited mechanical curiosity; from its connection with learning and its influence on the human character, it is certainly the most important invention with which the world has been benefited; and young people should endeavour to go through a printing-office after they have read this account of the art.

The workmen employed in printing are of two kinds: *compositors*, who range and dispose the letters into words, lines, pages, &c. according to the copy delivered to them by the author; and the *pressmen*, who apply ink upon the same, and take off the impression.

The letters, or, as they are usually called, the *types*, are made of a mixed metal; they are disposed in cases with separate square divisions, called boxes, for the different letters. There are two cases for the purpose of containing the types, called the upper and the lower case. In the upper are placed, in separate boxes or divisions, the capitals, small capitals, accented letters, figures, and the marks of reference; in the lower are placed the small letters, also the double letters, the stops, and the spaces that go between the words, and fill up short lines. A pair of cases for the Roman types, and another for the Italic, are usually placed on each frame, and they stand sloping, in such a manner as that every part shall be within the reach of the compositor. Having the letters properly distributed, he lays the written copy before him, and begins to compose. He has a small frame made of iron, called a composing-stick, in his left hand, in which he places the first letter of the first words of the copy, then the second, and so on till the word is finished; he then puts a blank or space between that and the next word: in this manner he proceeds till he has finished the line, when he goes on to the next; but all the letters are reversed, that the impression may stand right on the paper.

When the composing-stick, which holds several lines, is full, the compositor empties it carefully into a frame of wood called a *galley*. He then fills and empties the composing-stick as before, till a complete page is formed, when he ties it up with a cord or pack-thread, and, setting it by, proceeds to the next, till the number of pages to be contained in a sheet is completed; this being done, he carries them to the imposing-stone, there to be ranged in order, and fastened together in a frame called a *chase*; this is termed *imposing*. The chase is differently made, according to the number of pages contained in a sheet; that is, according as the work is folio, quarto, octavo, &c.

To dress the chase, is to range and fix the pages, leaving the proper margin between them: for this purpose the compositor makes use of a set of furniture, consisting of slips of wood of different dimensions; some of these are placed at the top of the pages, and called *head-sticks*; others at the sides, called *back-sticks* and *gutters*. The pages, being placed at their proper distances, are secured by the chase and furniture, and fastened together by means of little wedges of wood called *quoins*, driven between the chase and the foot and side-sticks with a wooden mallet and piece of hard wood. In this state the work is called a *form*; and as there are two forms required for every sheet, when both sides are to be printed, it is necessary that the distances between the pages in each form should be placed with such exactness, that the impression of the pages in one form shall fall exactly on the back of the pages of the other; this is called *register*.

As mistakes will occur, a sheet which is called a proof, is printed off, and given to the corrector of the press, who examines it while a boy reads the copy to him, making the requisite alterations in the margin; which being done, he gives the proof to the compositor to be corrected. This is done by unlocking the form upon the imposing-stone, loosening the quoins, and taking out the wrong or faulty letters marked in the proof, which he lays before him, with a slender sharp pointed steel bodkin, and putting others into their places. After this another proof is taken and, having been again read by the corrector, is sent to the author; who, if he wishes it, writes on it "*revise*," which signifies that another proof is to be sent to him, to see that all the mistakes marked in the last proof are corrected.

Here then the compositors's work is finished, and it is committed to the pressmen, whose business it is to work off the forms thus prepared and corrected; in doing which four things are required, viz. paper, ink, balls, and a press. To prepare the paper for use, it is first to be wetted, by dipping several sheets together in water; these are afterwards laid in a heap over each other, and, to make them take the water equally, they are all pressed down close with a weight at the top. The ink is made of oil and lamp-black. The balls, by which the ink is applied on the forms, are a kind of wooden funnels with handles, the cavities of which are filled with wool, and this is covered with undressed sheep-skin, made extremely soft and pliable. The pressman takes one of these in each hand, and, having applied one of them to the ink-block, works them together till the ink is equally distributed, and then he blackens the form which is placed on the press, by beating the face of the letter with the balls.

The printing-press is a complex and very curious machine, which will be readily understood by any person who is witness to the operation. Besides the machinery for pressing, there is a carriage, containing a large and polished stone, on which the form is placed this is rolled backwards and forwards to receive the sheet, and deliver it when the impression is made.

The form being laid on the stone and inked, the pressman takes a sheet of paper from the heap, and spreads it straight on a frame called a *tympan,* which confines two sheets of parchment and two folds of blanket between them: these are necessary to take the impression of the letters upon the paper. To the tympan is fastened, by hinges, a thin frame of iron called a *frisket,* which is covered with paper, cut in the necessary places, that the sheet, which is put between the tympan and the frisket, may receive the ink without injuring the margins. To regulate the margins, a sheet of paper is fastened on the tympan, and on each side is fixed an iron point, which makes holes in the sheet, and the points are placed in the same holes when the impression is to be made on the other side.

The carriage, containing the stone, form, paper, &c. is now, by turning a handle, rolled under the screw, which, with two pulls of the handle, performs the business; it is then rolled out again, and the paper taken off and laid on one side. The form is then again inked, and another sheet laid on as before; and this is continued till as many sheets are printed as the impression consists of. After one side of all the sheets is printed, another form, which contains the pages for the other side, is laid upon the press-stone, and printed off in the same manner.

In general there are two pressmen to each press; and then one man inks the form, and the other does the rest of the work. When the required number of sheets are taken off, the form is to be separated, in order that the letters may be restored to their proper cases. The form is first washed in a strong ley, by means of a stout brush, and then with fair water. It is then laid on a board by the compositor, who unlocks it, and, having loosened the lines, again washes it to free it completely from dirt. When he wants the types to compose another sheet, he takes out several lines at once upon a brass rule, and taking a word or two at a time between his finger and thumb, replaces each letter into its proper division, and this is called *distribution.*

Besides the several kinds of letters used in printing, there are likewise *rules* for black lines; borders; and head and tail-pieces. The rules for black lines are made of brass, and exactly of the height of the letter. Borders, flowers, &c. are ornaments in the form of long bars, serving for the divisions of books, chapters, &c. Head and tail-pieces are cut either in wood, pewter, brass, copper, or silver.

Journeymen printers, compositors and pressmen, will easily earn from thirty shillings to two guineas a week. The business of the pressman requires little genius, but a considerable portion of strength. A youth designed for a compositor ought to have been well educated in his own langugae; and he will find it of great advantage in the course of his business, if he understands something of the modern and the ancient languages.

THE BOOKBINDER

Bookbinding is said to be the art of sewing together the several sheets of a book, and securing them with a back and strong pasteboard sides, covered with leather. In this business, the first operation is to fold the sheets according to the proper form; that is, folios into two leaves, quartos into four, octavos into eight, and so on; this is usually the work of women, who perform it with a slip of ivory or boxwood, called a folding stick: in this they are directed by the catchwords and *signatures,* which are the letters with the numbers annexed to them, at the bottom of the pages of the first one or more leaves in each sheet.

The leaves thus folded and laid over each other in the order of the signature, are beaten on a stone with a heavy hammer, to make them solid and smooth, and then they are pressed. Thus prepared, they are sewed in a sewing-press, upon packthreads or cords, which are called bands, at a proper distance from each other; which is done by drawing a thread through the middle of each sheet, and giving a turn round each band, beginning with the first, and proceeding to the last. The common number of bands is six in folios, and five in quartos and octavos. In neat binding a saw is made use of, to make places for the bands, which are sunk into the paper, so that the back of the book, when bound, may be smooth, without any appearance of bands. After this the backs are glued, the ends of the bands being opened with a knife, for the more convenient fixing of the pasteboards; then the back is turned with a hammer, the book being fixed in a press between boards, called backing-boards, in order to make a groove for admitting the pasteboards. The boards being then applied, holes are made for drawing the bands through, the superfluous ends being cut off, and the parts hammered smooth. The book is then pressed, in order for cutting, which is performed by a machine called a plough. After this the book is put into a press called the cutting-press, betwixt two boards, the one lying even with the press, for the knife to run upon, the other above, for the knife to cut against.

The book being cut, the paste-boards are squared with a proper pair of iron shears, and it is then ready for sprinkling, gilding, blacking, or marbling the leaves. If the leaves are to be gilt, the book is put between two boards into a press, and when the leaves are rendered very smooth, they are rubbed over with size-water; the gold leaf is then laid on, dried by a fire, and burnished off.

The head-band is now to be added, which is an ornament of thread or silk, placed at the extremities of the book across the leaves, and woven or twisted about a roll of paper.

The book is now fit for covering: calf-skin is the most usual cover; this is moistened in water, and cut to the size of the book; the edges are then pared off on a marble stone. The cover is next smeared over with paste, then stretched over the paste-board on the outside, and doubled over the edges within-side. The bookbinder then fixes it firmly between two boards to make the cover stick the stronger to the pasteboards and the back; on the exact performance of which depends the neatness of the book. The back is now to be warmed by the first to soften the glue, and the leather of the back is rubbed down with a folding-stick or bodkin, to fix it close to the back of the book. After this, it is washed over with a little paste and water: two blank leaves on each side are then to be pasted down to the cover, and, when dry, the leaves are burnished in the press, and the cover rolled on the edges. The cover is now glazed with the white of an egg, and then polished with a polishing iron. If the book is to be lettered, a piece or pieces of red morocco are pasted between the bands, to receive the title, &c. in gold letters.

The letters or other ornaments are made with gilding-tools, engraved in *relievo,* either on the points of puncheons, or around little cylinders of brass, The puncheons make their impression by being pressed flat down, and the cylinders by being rolled along by a handle, to which they are fitted on an iron stay, or axis.

To apply the gold, the binders glaze the parts of the leather with a liquor made of the whites of eggs diluted with water, by means of a bit of sponge; and when nearly dry, they slightly oil them, and then lay on pieces of gold leaf; and on these they apply the tools, having first warmed them in a charcoal fire. When the gilding is finished, they rub off the superfluous gold, and polish the whole.

The business of the bookbinder, in general, requires no great ingenuity, nor any considerable strength of body. Journeymen can earn thirty shillings a week; and much more, if they are good workmen, and are intrusted with very fine work. Formerly bookbinding was not a separate trade, but it was united with that of the stationer; it is now, however, carried on alone, and bookbinders are generally employed constantly through the year.

The price of binding is regulated by certain printed lists agreed on between the bookseller and the book-binder.

In London, the business of gilding the leaves of books is a separate employment, and it is done before the boards of the book are covered with the leather.

THE CALLICO-PRINTER

Callico is a sort of cloth resembling linen, made of cotton; it takes its name from Callicut, a city on the coast of Malabar. The callico-printer is employed in printing this cloth. The first hint towards this branch of business was had from the Indian chintzes. The callico-printing was introduced into London in the year 1676, and it has since been encouraged by divers acts of parliament.

In the East Indies, they paint all their callicoes with the pencil, which they must do with great expedition, as the price there is very low; but here the following method is adopted: The pattern is first drawn on paper, the whole breadth of the cloth intended to be printed; the workman then divides the pattern into several parts according to its size, each part being about eight inches broad, by twelve inches long; each distinct part of the pattern thus divided, is cut out upon wooden blocks; the cloth to be printed is extended upon a table; and the types, being covered with the proper colours, are laid on and the impression is left upon the cloth. The workman begins to lay on the types at one end of the piece, and so continues till the whole is finished: great care must be taken that the patterns join with accuracy, and that there is no interstice or vacancy left.

Cutting the pattern in wood being the most curious part of the process, we shall describe that particularly. The cutters in wood begin with preparing a plank or block of the proper size: beech, pear-tree, and box, are used for this purpose; but the box-tree is the most fit for the business, as being the closest, and least liable to be worm-eaten. As soon as the wood is cut into the proper size and made very smooth, it is fit to receive the drawing of the design. Sometimes ink is used, and to prevent its running, it is rubbed over with a mixure of white lead and water, and after it is dry it is rubbed off and polished.

On this the design is drawn; and those who cannot draw themselves, make use of designs furnished by others whose profession is to draw patterns. The drawing marks out so much of the block as is to be spared, or left standing. The rest they cut off, and take away very curiously with the point of exceedingly sharp knives, or little chisels, or gravers, according to the bigness or delicacy of the work; for they stand in need of no other instruments.

Block-engraving differs from that on copper, in this: that in the former the impression comes from the prominent parts, or strokes left un-cut; whereas in the latter it comes from channels cut in the metal.

The manner of printing with wooden prints is easy and expeditious, if there be only two colours; as green and blue; or black, and a white ground, then the block requires only to be dipped in the printing-ink, and impressed on the cloth. If more colours are used, then they are to be laid on with a brush or brushes, and the impressions to be made as before with the hand.

When the whole piece is printed, the cloth is washed and bleached to take away any accidental stains it may have acquired in the operation: it is then dried, calendered, and laid up in folds fit for the shop.

Callico-printing is reckoned a very good business both for the master and his journeyman: the master, however, requires a large capital, a situation plentifully supplied with good and clear water, and extensive grounds for bleaching and drying their cloths. He employs three sorts of hands; the pattern-drawer; the cutters of the type, who are also the operators in printing; and a number of labourers, to assist in washing. The pattern-drawer is paid according to the variety and value of the designs; and the printer, who is able also to cut with ability and taste, can, in the summer months, earn four or five guineas a week, or more.

A youth designed for this business ought to have a genius for drawing, a good eye, and a delicate hand. The business is not laborious, and the chief care is in the choice of a master who will do justice to his apprentice. Most callico-printers have some particular secrets in the preparation of their colours, which they ought to be bound to reveal to those whom they undertake to teach the art; since on the knowledge of this depends principally the success of the lad.

What are called wood-engravings are done after this manner, and so are paper-hangings, and playing-cards. But card-making is purely a mechanical business, and requires neither judgement, strength, or ingenuity.

THE TIN-PLATE WORKER

Tin-plate, or tin, as it is usually called, is a composition of iron and block-tin, not melted together, but the iron, in bars, is cased over with tin, and then flatted or drawn out by means of mills.

In the year 1681, tin-plates were made in England by Andrew Yarranton, who was sent into Bohemia to learn the art. The manufacture did not seem to answer, and was even reckoned among the projects called bubbles in 1720: in a very few years it was again revived; and in the year 1740 it was brought to such perfection, that very small quantities have since that time been imported. Our plates are of a finer gloss, or coat, than those made beyond sea, the latter being chiefly hammered, but ours are always drawn out by the rolling-mill.

The tin-plate worker receives it in sheets, and it is his business to form them in all the various articles that are represented in the plate, such as kettles, saucepans, canisters of all sorts and sizes, milk-pails, lanthorns, &c. &c.

The instruments that he makes use of are, a large pair of shears to cut the tin into the proper size and shape, a polished anvil, and hammers of various kinds. The joints of his work he makes with *solder*, which is a composition of what is called *block-tin* and lead; this he causes to unite with the tin, by means of rosin.

The business of a tin-plate worker is very profitable to the master: and the journeyman, if sober and industrious, can with ease earn from thirty-five shillings to two guineas a week. The principal manufacturers in London, are Jones and Taylor's, in Tottenham-court-road, and Howards', in Old-street. These seldom employ less than one hundred, or a hundred and fifty men each. Those who manufacture tin-ware on a small scale may be found in every part of the metropolis; and one of the chief sources of profit which these smaller tradesmen enjoy, is that of lamp-lighting.

This business does not require great strength; but if a man would carry it on upon a large scale it requires a very considerable capital: journeymen's wages may amount to between two and three hundred pounds per week. In fact, the tin-plate-worker pays his men twice a week: for on the Wednesday night a bell is rung which announces to each workman, that the master or his chief clerk is ready in the counting-house, to lend money to those who cannot wait till Saturday night for their wages.

The large houses have constantly travellers in various parts of the kingdom; and, as they cannot carry the articles of their trade in saddle-bags, they have drawings of all works of taste, such as moulds for jellies, puddings, &c.

Tin in blocks resembles silver, but is darker. It is softer, less elastic, and sonorous, than any other metal, except lead. It is easily extended into leaves, and melts more readily than all the metals. A composition of eight parts of bismuth, five of lead, and three of tin, will melt in boiling water. When tin is made pretty hot it will break with a blow. In the ore, tin is mixed with arsenic.

Tin, being less liable to rust than iron, copper, or lead, is advantageously used for the inside covering of metallic vessels. An amalgam of tin and mercury is used to cover the back surface of looking-glasses.

The chief tin-mines in the known world are those in Cornwall. It is a fact well ascertained, that the Phenicians visited these islands, for the purpose of getting tin, some centuries before the Christian era. In the time of King John, the Cornwall mines produced but little, the right of working them being at that period wholly in the King, as Earl of Cornwall. Their value has fluctuated at different periods: about a century ago they did not yield above thirty or forty thousand pounds per annum; but of late years they have produced five times that sum. The Prince of Wales, as Duke of Cornwall, receives four shillings upon every hundred weight of what is called *coined* white tin: this amounts to about ten thousand pounds per annum. The proprietors of the soil have one sixth, and the rest goes to the adventurers in the mine, who are at the whole charge of working.

The tin being to be divided among the lords and adventurers, is stamped and worked at the mill, and is then carried, under the name of block-tin, to the melting-house, where it is melted and poured into blocks or bars, and carried to the coinage town.

The coinage towns are Leskard, Lestwithiel, Truro, Helston, and Penzance, being the most convenient parts of the county for the tinners to bring their tin to every quarter of a year.

THE BRAZIER

This artificer makes kettles, pails, candlesticks, and other kitchen utensils in brass. In the shops we often find, that the same people deal in brass, copper, and tin ware; and not unfrequently, the furnishing iron-monger sells almost every article made in brass and copper, particularly in large country towns. In such cases the brazier neither makes, nor is supposed to make, all the different articles in his shop; it is sufficient for his own purpose, as well as for the advantage of his customers, that he should be so much of a working brazier, as to be a competent judge of the workmanship of all the goods in which he deals. If he is a master in a large way, he employs a great number of his hands in the different branches of his trade, and his profits are, of course, in proportion to the magnitude of his capital.

Some of the articles manufactured by the working brazier are beat out with the hammer, and united in their several parts by solder; others are cast; those which are cast belong to the business of the *founder,* except the polishing and finishing, which require the art of the brazier.

The working brazier has need of strength, and, if he would excel in his profession, he should possess ingenuity, to finish his work with taste.

The *Founder* is employed in casting a thousand different articles in brass; for which purpose he has models of the work designed: to these he fits the mould in which he casts his metal. He rarely designs anything himself, and his chief skill lies in melting the brass, and running it into the mould evenly. There are various kind of founders; some who cast for braziers only, others who cast the different smaller articles for coachmakers, sadlers, &c. and some cast the brass cannon, to carry on the dreadful art of war.

The Founder requires a strong constitution to undergo the heat of immense furnaces: he may earn thirty shillings per week: but it frequently happens that he spends a large portion of it in porter.

Brass is not a simple metal, but compounded of copper and zinc in certain proportions, if the proportion of copper is greater, the compound is Pinchbeck. Copper alloyed with tin makes bronze, bell-metal, &c.

Copper is dug out of the earth, or found united with many springs containing a portion of sulphuric acid. The richest copper-mines in the known world are in the Isle of Anglesea. The mountain from which the ore is dug is called Parys; and from it have been dug thirty thousand tons in a year. There are two springs at Herngrundt, in Upper Hungary, so richly impregnated with copper and sulphuric acid, that iron thrown into them is dissolved by the acid, and the copper falls to the bottom in its metallic form. Near these springs, pits are dug, and filled with the water: old iron is then thrown into them which, in about a fortnight or three weeks, is taken out, and the copper scraped off. By this process, a hundred pounds of iron will produce from eight to ninety pounds of copper. The same method is adopted at some springs in the county of Wicklow, in Ireland, and here twenty pounds of iron will yield sixteen of copper, which fetches a high price.

The Coppersmith makes coppers, boilers, and all manner of large vessels for brewers, distillers, and others. His work is very laborious, and the business is the most noisy of all mechanical employments. The wages of the journeymen are equal to the powers of body required in the operations.

Copper is used in a variety of the arts: but vessels made of it for culinary purposes are highly prejudicial: for acid and fatty substances, when left in them any time, combine with the copper, and form verdigrease, which is an absolute poison, and when taken in the smallest quantities it is very prejudicial to the constitution.

To prevent these pernicious effects, most copper vessels are well tinned on their insides. This operation is thus effected: The surface is well cleaned, by rubbing it with sal-ammoniac, or an acid; the tin, or a composition of tin and lead, is then melted in the vessel, and rubbed well about it with old rags, doubled up.

THE BUTTON-MAKER

There are several kinds of buttons some made of gold and silver lace, others of mohair, silk, &c. and others of metal. The process of stamping metal buttons is very simple, after the metal comes out of the founder's hands.

The pieces of metal are either cast or cut to the proper size, and then sent to the button-maker, who has dies or stamps according to the pattern wanted. The man stands in a place lower than the floor, by which he is nearer on a level with the place on which his dies stand: by means of a single pulley he raises a weight to the lower part of which is fixed another die; he lets the weight fall down the metal, and the thing is done. After this operation they are to be shanked, which is performed by means of solder; they are then polished by women. At Birmingham this manufacture is carried on upon a very large scale. The late John Taylor, Esq. was the inventor of gilt buttons; and in his house buttons have been manufactured to the amount of 500l. per week.

Besides those cast in a mould, there are great quantities of buttons made of thin plates. The plates are brought to a proper degree of thickness by the rolling-mill: they are then cut into round pieces of the size wanted. Each piece of metal thus cut, is reduced to the form of a button by beating it in several spherical cavities, beginning with the flattest cavity,and proceeding to the more spherical, till the plate has got all the *relievo* required; and, the more readily to manage so thin a plate, ten or a dozen of them are formed to the cavities at once. As soon as the inside is formed, an impression is given to the outside, by working it with an iron puncheon, in a kind of mould like minters' coins, engraven indentedly, and fastened to a block or bench. The cavity of the mould in which the impression is to be made, is of a diameter and depth suitable to the sort of button to be struck in it; each kind requiring a particular mould.

The plate thus prepared makes the upper part or shell of the button. The lower part is formed of another plate, made after the same manner, but flatter, and without any impression. To this is soldered a little eye, made of wire, for the button to be fastened by.

The two plates are soldered together with a wooden mould, covered with wax or rosin between, to render the button solid and firm; for the wax or other cement entering all the cavities formed by the *relievo* of the other side, sustains it, prevents its flattening, and preserves its design.

The art of button-making in its various branches is encouraged and protected by divers acts of parliament. It is unlawful to import foreign buttons. And buttons made of, or covered with, cloth, cannot be worn, without subjecting the wearer to very severe penalties, if any person choose to sue for the same.

Glass buttons are composed of glass of various colours. The glass is kept in fusion, and the button nipt out of it while in a state of fusion by a pair of iron moulds, like those for casting shot, adapted to the intended form of the button, the shank having been inserted in the mould, so that it may become imbedded in the glass when cool.

THE CABINET-MAKER

The cabinet-maker is but a superior kind of carpenter; he works neater, is employed on better materials, and his gains, whether considered as a master or journeyman, are probably much greater than those of a common carpenter.

All the arts of life have, no doubt, been the result of a gradual and progressive improvement in civilization. In nothing is this exhibited more than in an upholsterer's ware-house. What a difference is there between the necessary articles of furniture to be found in a cottage, and the elegantly furnished house of a merchant or a peer! In the former, there is nothing but what is plain, useful, and almost essential to the convenience of life: in the latter, immense sums are sacrificed to magnificence and show. The cottager is content with a deal table, an oaken chair, and a beachen bedstead, with other articles equally plain and unexpensive. The wealthy possess sumptuous beds, inlaid tables, silk or damask chairs and curtains, sofas, and carpets of great value; large looking-glasses, and brilliant lustres; together with a variety of carved work and gilding. The furniture of a cottage, or of a small farm-house, will cost but a few guineas; that of a single room in the wealthy parts of the metropolis, will be valued at from five hundred to a thousand pounds.

The cabinet-maker furnishes chairs, tables, chests of drawers, desks, scrutoires, bureaus, and book-cases, of all sorts and prices. But in almost all places the business of the cabinet-maker is united to that of the upholsterer: and the furniture collected in one of their warehouses is worth from ten to thirty thousand pounds. Such warehouses may be seen in St. Paul's Church-yard, Bond-street, and other parts of London.

The cabinet-maker's chief tools are, saws, axes, planes, chissels, files, gimlets, turn-screws, hammers, and other tools, which are used in common by the carpenter and the cabinet-maker: but those adapted to the latter are much finer than the tools required by the house-carpenter. The wood principally used by cabinet-makers is mahogany, which has been described under the article Carpenter.

Glue, which is of great use to the cabinet-maker, is made of the skins of animals, as oxen, sheep, &c. and the older the animal is the better the glue. Whole skins are rarely used for this purpose, but only the shavings and parings made by curriers, fellmongers, &c. These are boiled to the consistence of jelly, and poured into flat moulds to cool; it is then cut into square pieces, and hung up to dry.

The goodness and the value of furniture depend on the fineness of the wood, and other materials of which it is made, and on the neatness of the workmanship. A young man brought up to this business should possess a good share of ingenuity, and talents for drawing and designing; because much depends on fashion, and in pleasing the various tastes of the public.

THE SADLER

In early ages, when the horse was trained to the use of man, the rider sat on the bare back of the animal; but in the course of time, a covering was used, which consisted of a dressed or undressed skin of some beast slaughtered for food. Such coverings became afterwards very costly; they were decorated with many ornaments, and made large enough to hang down nearly to the ground.

Six lions' hides with thongs together fast
His upper parts defended to his waist;
And where man ended, the continued vest
Spread on his back the house and trappings of a beast.

DRYDEN.

But it was reckoned, among the Romans, more manly to ride on the bare back than upon coverings; and Xenophon, in his Cyropaedia, reproaches the Persians for placing more clothes on the backs of their horses than on their beds; and giving themselves more trouble to sit easily than to ride skilfully.

Saddles, as they are now made, are seats adapted to a horse's back, for the convenience of the rider. They consist of a wooden frame called the saddle-tree, on which is laid a quantity of horse-hair, wool, &c; and this is covered over with tanned leather, neatly nailed to the wooden tree. To keep the saddle steady on the horse, the crupper is used, which passes under the creature's tail; and girths, to prevent it from turning round. To support the legs of the rider, a pair of stirrups is also added, one of which is very useful in assisting to mount the animal: and to prevent the saddle from galling the horse's back. The articles made use of in the manufacture of these things, are more or less costly, according to the price that the purchaser pays for his goods.

Cutting-knives, hammers, and pincers, are the chief implements of the trade; that is, of the person employed in the manufacture of saddles. To complete a single article in the business, the aid of many different artisans is required.

The tree-maker furnishes only the wooden part of the saddle: this is, however, a very important branch of the business; because upon the saddle-tree the fitting of the saddle depends; and in cases when gentlemen wish to have their saddles fit properly, it is as necessary to measure the horses's back, as for the shoemaker to measure his customers for boots or shoes. The saddle-tree maker requires no great strength nor ingenuity.

The sadler's ironmonger furnishes him with the iron or steel stirrups, buckles of all kinds, bits for bridles, and other steel or brass furniture required for the harness of a horse, either for riding or drawing in a carriage. Many of these articles are originally made by the iron-founder.

There is also a distinct trade called a horse's milliner, who makes roses for bridles, and other articles used in highly ornamented caparisons. This tradesman should have an inventive genius, and a considerable share of taste to set off the furniture belonging to a horse, and decorate it in a neat and elegant style.

The journeymen, in almost every branch of the sadlery business, work by the piece, and may earn a good living: they none of them require great strength; the men always work in the dry, and in most of the branches cleanliness, which is no small requisite in the mechanical arts, is a principal characteristic.

The sadler makes all sorts of bridles, coach and chaise harness: of course, besides the trades already noticed as peculiarly belonging to his business, he employs the tanner or leather-cutter; the currier; the embroiderer, who works devices, crests, and coats of arms in gold, silver, or worsteds. He buys broadcloths and other woollens of the draper, velvet and silk of the mercer, ribbons of the weaver, gold and silver and livery lace from the laceman; buckram, thread, &c. from the haberdasher. Of all these articles he should, for the sake of his customers, be a good judge. The master requires a considerable capital, if he is in a large way, and called upon to give much credit.

A great number of saddles are exported into foreign parts, particularly to the East Indies, as English-made saddles are in great repute there.

There are many different kinds of saddles, as the hunting-saddle, the racing-saddle, ladies'-saddles, &c.

Saddles are of considerable antiquity: at Berne, about a century ago, a saddle used to be shown as the same on which Julius Caesar rode; and in the fourth century, the emperor Theodosius forbad the use of saddles weighing more than sixty pounds.

THE GLASS-BLOWER

There is scarcely any manufacture of more real utility than that of glass. It is formed of sand and salt mixed in proper proportions, and melted in a furnace. Sea-sand is generally used for the purpose, and the salt is an alkali procured from the burning of sea-weeds.

The furnace is round, and has several apertures, in one of which the fuel is introduced; the others serve to lade out the melted metal.

When the ingredients of which glass is composed are perfectly fused, and have acquired the necessary degree of heat, part of the melted matter is taken out at the end of a hollow tube, about two feet and a half long, which is dipped into it, and turned about, till a sufficient quantity is taken up; the workman then rolls it gently upon a piece of iron, to unite it more intimately. He then blows through the tube, till the melted mass at the extremity swells into a bubble; after which he again rolls it on a smooth surface, to polish it, and repeats the blowing, till the glass is brought as near the size and form of the vessel required as he thinks necessary.

There are three principal kinds of glasses, distinguished by the form or manner of working them, viz. round glass, as bottles, drinking glasses, &c.; table, or window glass,— of this also there are several kinds; and plate-glass.

If a bottle is to be formed, the melted glass at the end of the tube is put into a mould of the exact size and shape of its body, and the neck is formed on the outside, by drawing out the ductile glass.

If it be a vessel with a *wide orifice,* the glass, in its melted state, is opened and widened with an iron tool; after which, being again heated, it is whirled about with a circular motion, till it is extended to the size required. If a handle, foot, or any thing else of the kind be required, these are made separately, and stuck on in the melted state.

Window-glass is formed in a similar manner, except that the liquid mass at the end of the tube is blown into a cylindrical shape, which, being cut longtitudinally by a pair of scissars or sheers, is gradually bent until it becomes a flat place. The best window-glass was, till within these few years, made at Radcliffe: but this manufactory is now abandoned, and the crown-glass is brought from Newcastle, as well as the green glass.

Plate-glass, for looking-glasses, is made by suffering the mass in a state of complete fusion to flow upon a table with iron ledges to confine the melted matter, and, as it cools, a metallic roller is passed over it, to reduce it to an uniform thickness.

Glass is sometimes coloured, by mixing it with, while in a fluid state, various metallic oxydes. It is coloured blue by the oxyde of colbalt; red, by the oxyde of copper or iron; yellow, by the oxyde of silver or antimony; and violet, by the oxyde of manganese.

Though glass, when cold, is brittle, it is one of the most ductile bodies known. When liquid, if a thread of melted glass be drawn out and fastened to a reel, the whole of the glass may be spun off; and by cutting the threads of a certain length, there is obtained a sort of feather of glass. A thread of glass may be drawn or spun so fine as to be scarcely visible to the naked eye. Glass is very elastic and sonorous. Fluoric acid dissolves it, and the alkalis act upon it.

Glass utensils require to be gradually cooled in an oven: this operation, called annealing, is necessary to prevent them from breaking, by change of temperature, wiping, &c.

The glazier buys the glass which he uses, at the glass-house, in crates, which contain twelve, fifteen, or eighteen tables each, according to the goodness of the glass; these he cuts into pieces or panes, with a diamond fixed in a ferule. There are two kinds of windows, namely, those in which the glass is fastened in wood, and those in which it is fixed in lead: the glazier makes use of putty, a composition of linseed-oil and whiting, for the former: for the latter the lead is first cast into thin pieces of fifteen inches long, and about a quarter of an inch thick; and then these are passed through a vice, which draws them out to the length of about four feet. The glass is fixed in grooves made in the lead, and the lead soldered together with a composition made of lead and block-tin.

Plate-glass comes from the manufactory in a very rough state; it is scarcely transparent. It is then ground with sand and polished with *emery,* which is a mineral substance, and *putty* formed of lead and tin calcined together. This last substance is the principal thing used in forming white enamels, and glazings for earthen-ware.

When the glass plate is polished, it is to be silvered for a reflecting or looking-glass, which is done in the following manner: A large and very even board is prepared, on this is spread very evenly some tin-foil, and on the tin-foil is spread quick-silver; the glass is then laid on the quicksilver, and a number of leaden weights, covered with baize, are laid upon the glass; in this state it remains several days, till the tin and quick-silver adhere firmly to the glass.

Glass-makers can only work in the cold months, owing to the great heats of their furnaces their wages are large in proportion to the disadvantages attending their labours.

Glaziers, in London, make a considerable proportion of their profits by window-cleaning: the journeymen earn about four shillings a day.

Glass-grinders and polishers work by the piece, and may get a good living, considering that little more ingenuity is required than that which is necessary for common labours.

With respect to the composition of glass, it may be observed, that *flint*-glass is formed of soda, pounded flints, and the oxyde of lead. Crown or window glass contains no lead, it consists of soda and fine sand. Bottle-glass is the coarsest of all, and is composed of kelp and common sand. Of these the most fusible is the flint glass, and the least fusible the bottle glass.

THE CORK-CUTTER

Cork is the bark of a tree of the same name. It is a species of oak. It grows thirty or forty feet high, having a thick, rough, and fungous bark: its leaves are green above, and white underneath, and its fruit is an acorn, which is produced in great abundance. The bark of this tree is taken off by making an incision from the top to the bottom, and likewise one at each extremity round the tree, and perpendicular to the first. The old bark being thus detached, the tree still lives, and in six or seven years a succeeding bark is again fit for use.

The bark when stripped from the tree is piled up in a pit or pond, and loaded with heavy stones to flatten it; it is then taken to be dried, when it is fit for sale. The tree is not in the smallest degree injured by the operation of peeling off the bark; for if it be not performed, it splits and peels off of itself, being pushed up by another bark from underneath. The cork-tree is found in great abundance in France, Spain, and Italy: from these countries we receive the bark.

The cork-cutters business requires but little ingenuity; the knives used in the operation have a peculiar construction, and they must be exceedingly sharp. The knife is almost the only instrument wanted in the trade. The principal demand for corks is for the purpose of stopping bottles; these are cut by men and women, who receive a certain price *per gross* for their labour. Cork-cutters sell also corks by the gross. It is one of the blackest and dirtiest of all the trades, and not very profitable either for the master or the journeyman.

Cork is likewise used by young people in learning the art of swimming. The cork waistcoat is composed of four pieces of cork; two for the breasts, and two for the back, each nearly as long as a waistcoat without flaps. The cork is covered, and adapted to fit the body. It is open before, and may be fastened either with strings, or buckles and straps. The waistcoat weighs about twelve ounces, and may be made at the expence of a few shillings. This article of dress would be very useful to all persons who travel much by water, or who are in the habit of bathing in the open sea. Cork is also used for the inner soles of shoes.

A cork spencer has lately been invented to save persons from drowning, in cases of shipwreck. It consists of a belt, containing refuse-pieces of cork, inclosed in any kind of covering, and fastened round the body with tapes.

In Spain, cork is burnt to make that light kind of black, called Spanish black, which is very much used by painters. The Egyptians make their coffins of cork: and these, when lined with a certain resinous composition, preserve the dead a great length of time. In Spain they even line the walls of their houses with cork, which not only renders the apartment warm, but corrects the moisture of the air.

Cork, when burnt and reduced to powder, is often taken internally as an astringent; and it has been said, that cups made of cork are useful for hectic persons to drink their common beverage from.

Fossil-cork is the name given to a kind of stone, which is the lightest of all stones; it is a species of amianthus, consisting of flexible fibres, loosely interwoven, and resembling the vegetable cork; it is fusible in the fire, and forms a black glass.

THE WATCH-MAKER

This business has not been known in England more than a century and a half; but now the best watches in the world are made in London, and an immense exportation trade in this article is carried on here.

When watches were first made, the whole business was performed by one man, who was then properly called a watch-maker; but the name is now given to him who puts the various movements together, adjusts their several parts, and finishes the whole machine.

It is only about a century ago when watches went upon cat-gut instead of a chain; but cat-gut was materially affected by every change in the atmosphere, and of course the watch could not measure accurate time for two days together: but since the invention of the chain, and the great improvement in the temper of the springs, our watches are but little affected by the weather in this climate.

Watches and clocks being adapted to the same purpose, are made, or rather finished, by the same artizan. The *former* are such movements as *shew* the parts of time; the *latter* are such as *publish* it, by striking on a bell. But the name of watches is usually appropriated to such as are carried in the pocket; and that of clocks to the larger movements whether they strike the hour or not. Watches that strike the hour are called repeating-watches.

Watches and clocks are composed of wheels and pinions; in the former there is a balance, or regulator, to direct the quickness and slowness of the wheels, and a spring which communicates motion to the whole machine: but in clocks, instead of the regulator and spring, there are a pendulum and two weights. The spring of a watch is inclosed in a barrel, on the outside of which is wound a chain: one end of this chain is fixed to the barrel itself, and the other to the fusee, which is a piece of metal in the form of a cone.

When a watch is wound up, the chain which was upon the barrel winds upon the fusee, and by this means the spring in the barrel is stretched; for the interior end of the spring is fixed to an immoveable axis, about which the barrel revolves. The spring, being made of exceedingly elastic steel, endeavours to recover its former position, which forces the barrel to turn round; this motion obliges the chain, which is upon the fusee, to unfold, and turn the fusee. The motion of the fusee is communicated to a wheel, which, by means of its teeth connected with the pinion, turns another wheel, and so of the rest.

The parts of a watch are made by several different mechanics. The *movement-maker* forges the wheels in solid metal to the exact dimensions; from him they go to the person who cuts the teeth. This part of the operation was formerly done by hand; and perhaps one of the greatest improvements that watches and clocks ever received, was the invention of engines for cutting the teeth. This has reduced the expence of workmanship and time to a mere trifle, in comparison of what it was before, and has besides brought the work to a degree of exactness which no hand can imitate.

The wheels come back from the cutter to the movement-maker, who finishes them, and turns the corners of the teeth. The steel pinions are drawn at a mill, so that the watch-maker has only to file down the pivots, and fix them to the proper wheels.

The watch-springs form a trade of themselves: they are prepared by forming a very thin plate of steel into a double ring, bending it round with wire, and putting it in a proper furnace, to give it a suitable degree of heat. It is then dropped into oil or melted fat, which gives it a hardness equal to that of glass; it then undergoes several other operations to bring it to that fine colour and polish which it possesses.

The chains are made principally by women, who cut them at a certain and a small price per dozen. It requires no great ingenuity to learn the art of making watch-chains; the instruments made use of render the work easy, which at first sight appears very difficult.

There are workmen also, who make nothing else than the caps and studs for watches; and others who make the cases, and others who cut and enamel the dial plates. A particular set of tradesmen are called watch-tool makers, because their whole business consists in forming implements used by watch and clock-makers.

When the watch-maker has got home all the movement of the watch, and the other different parts of which it consists, he gives them to a finisher, who puts the whole together, and adjusts it to proper time.

All the branches of this profession require a considerable share of ingenuity, and a light hand to touch those delicate instruments which are requisite in their trade. The watch-finisher not only wants a strong sight, but is obliged to make use of magnifying glasses, the frames of which are adapted to the shape of the socket of the eye. Few trades, if any, require a quicker eye or a steadier hand.

The trade in watches is very considerable; of course it employs a great number of hands, and the profits of master and men are considerable. A man to be scientific watch-maker, should understand the principles of mechanics, and something of mathematics; a lad, therefore, intended for this business, should have a mechanical genius and a good education.

Clock-making differs chiefly from watch-making only in the size of the work; so that a person who is conversant in the latter is equally fitted for the former.

There are two very curious and celebrated clocks at Strasburg and Lyons. In the former, a cock claps his wings and proclaims the hours, and an angel opens a door, and salutes the virgin. In the latter, two horsemen encounter, and beat the hour on each other; a door opens, and there appear on the theatre the Virgin with Jesus Christ in her arms, and two trumpeters to proclaim the procession.

There are many tradesmen in London, chiefly foreigners, who make a good living by the manufacture of wooden clocks; here every wheel, as well as the sides, is made of wood, and, excepting some wire and the striking-bell, there is nothing but wood that goes into the construction of those machines, which are sold as low as five shillings each; a very good one may be had for ten or twelve shillings. To these are often attached *alarums;* they then become useful for servants, to awaken them in the morning.

CONTENTS of PART I